C000177769

Bristlenoses

Catfish with Character

Kathy Jinkings

t.f.h.
KINGDOM

contents

Acknowledgements 4

Introduction 5

1 Classification and relationships 9

2 Biology of the Bristlenose 21

3 Bristlenoses at home 35

4 Keeping Bristlenoses in the aquarium 47

5 Spawning the Bristlenose 62

6 Species of Bristlenose 76

Appendix 1 - Collection locations of *Ancistrus* species 99

Literature 107

Index 111

Acknowledgements

This book has been made possible by the assistance of a large number of people who have given their time, expertise and encouragement. I would like to thank:

Bill Hurst and the members of the Northern Area Catfish Group who inspired the whole thing. This entire project started as research for a lecture that got out of hand!

Oliver Crimmen and all the staff at the London Natural History Museum who supplied advice, helped me track down information and prepared the *ranunculus* specimen featured in many of the photographs.

Erwin Schraml who uncomplainingly engaged in long and extended e-mail correspondences about identification of fish and also for the use of his photographs.

Dr David Sands for encouragement and access to his documentation and works, and for providing some of the photographs in this book (including the front page and title page photographs).

Tom Clayton for translating the German documents for me - and he doesn't even like fish!

Sue Dilley for advice on photography and for taking the photographs of the *ranunculus* alizarin preparation.

Paul and all the staff at Swallow Aquatics in Colchester who lent me a variety of fish for photography and who continue to obtain weird and wonderful bristlenoses for me.

Eddie and all the staff at SeaPets in Colchester for lending various bits of equipment for photography.

Introduction

Whilst setting up my first aquarium, I spent many happy hours wandering around fish shops gazing at the plethora of beautiful fish on show. Guppies trailed spectacular fins seductively while flashing tetras caught the eye with luminous gleams. Amidst this display of colour I noticed a sad and ugly brown fish trying to cram itself, unsuccessfully, behind a filter tube. This was my first, inauspicious, sight of a bristlenose.

***Ancistrus* sp.**

The aquarium was finally purchased and stocked with many beautiful fish. It wasn't long before green algae, the curse of the beginner, started its march across the front glass. Treatments and scrubbing only resulted in a temporary hiatus in its growth and the beautiful fish were no longer so beautiful seen through a green veil. On returning to the

Bristlenoses are always hungry and are champion algae-cleaners.

shop the large bristlenose I had seen earlier had been sold, and all they could offer me were two overpriced and undersized (to my way of thinking) tiny little scraps of fish which, I was assured, were baby bristlenoses. They were released into the green murk and quickly vanished. After a few days, there were patches on the glass that were clear. A few days more, and larger windows were apparent. I could see my fish again! Over the following weeks, the two tiny fish dedicated themselves to algae-eating like two little animated lawn-mowers. Within a remarkably short space of time the tank was entirely cleaned up and, after a bit of work with a razor blade to remove a few spots of hardened algae, looked brand new. In the midst of the pristine tank were two fat bristlenoses, now each about two inches long, evidently wondering where the inexhaustible food supply had gone.

Now that I could see them, the charm of these fish rapidly became apparent. I discovered that bristlenoses are not seen to their advantage in shop tanks, frightened and deprived of cover. At home, feeling secure and with plenty of hiding places if they should need them, they were constantly seen out and about, usually in a never-ending search for food. Once all the algae had gone, they switched happily to a diet of green

Bristlenoses can become active and visible members of a community aquarium.

foodstuff and catfish pellets, rushing to the front as soon as anyone approached on the chance that a meal was in the offing. Sometimes they couldn't wait until the food was put down for them and would latch on to my hand while I was attempting to position it. The dull brown fright coloration disappeared, to reveal a pattern of pale spots on dark brown. While they will never have the flashy beauty of guppies or neon tetras they are certainly not unattractive. Within a year they were full size fish, at around five inches long. Luckily enough, they turned out to be a pair and presented me that winter with a large crop of bright orange eggs which the male guarded patiently until they hatched.

Since these events occurred, many more tanks have been added to my collection, and many new species of fish have made their appearance. Other species have lost interest, and are no longer a feature. The war against algae has been won. However, each tank still has at least one pair of bristlenoses in residence, including the original pair who are still eating and breeding with undiminished enthusiasm.

Apart from their usefulness in clearing up algae and food that falls to the bottom, and an endearing personality, bristlenoses have held my interest because they are remarkably interesting fish. What once appeared to my novice eyes as ugliness is, in fact, the result of a remarkable series of adaptations, each making them a little bit more efficient at conducting their chosen way of life. An increasing number of imports results

***Ancistrus* sp.**

in new species appearing almost on a weekly basis, many of which are undescribed and have not yet been spawned in the aquarium. More than with any other type of fish I have kept, there is always something new to observe and learn. Although there has been a reasonable amount of research into this family, much of it is buried in scientific papers and is not easily accessible to the hobbyist; there are many questions that still remain unanswered.

The bristlenose is a fish for everyone, from the beginner who wants an easy-to-keep fish to the dedicated hobbyist who wishes to learn as much as possible about his charges. Similarly, I have intended this book to be for everyone. For those who have not yet discovered the delights of the bristlenose, I hope that it will inspire you to give a pair a home in your tank and be led by your fish into the ranks of those whose interest runs a little deeper. For those who are already confirmed fans, this is the result of my own quest for understanding of these fish which I hope will enable you to understand and appreciate your fish a little better.

This is not the complete book of the bristlenose; such a book can never be written as there will always be something new to discover. New information is not solely the province of scientists. The contribution of hobbyists to our knowledge is immense and everyone can contribute to the ever increasing pool by learning from the best teachers - your fish.

Classification and relationships 1

What has it got to do with me?

Many aquarium hobbyists feel that scientific classifications (and, indeed, science in general) have no relevance to their hobby. On the contrary, however, there are a large number of benefits to be gained from at least a passing familiarity.

By understanding how a particular fish fits into the grand scheme and knowing about its relationships with other fish species, it is possible to make an educated guess as to how to keep and breed it if no specific information is available about that species. Furthermore, if you need to look up more information, discuss your fish with another hobbyist or an expert, or even order a new fish from the shop, it is extremely useful if both parties are referring to the same species of fish. Common names, such as 'bristlenose' and 'pleco' are often applied indiscriminately to a variety of species and ordering one from a shop is akin to entering a lucky dip.

You will see as you read through the book that there are still many questions to be answered about different bristlenose species and their lifestyles. Knowledge is not elitist and, if you observe new and interesting behaviour, or succeed in spawning a new import, then it is your duty to share that information. The people you tell will want to know exactly what it is you are talking about, so that they can try to achieve the same results. Scientific names and jargon are an important part of that communication and a working familiarity is not difficult to achieve.

The great pattern of life

The simplest way to describe anything is by comparison with other, similar things. We use this method in our daily lives to describe everything from colour to food. Living organisms are a bit more difficult to describe than fried chicken so, to make such a vast topic manageable, all life (both current and extinct) fits into a huge system of classification. The system we use at present was developed by Linnaeus in a series of publications starting in 1735. The new system included 'binomial nomenclature', using both the genus and species name to uniquely identify an organism. Of course, science has advanced a great deal since then and many people have expanded the original system to incorporate new information and understanding.

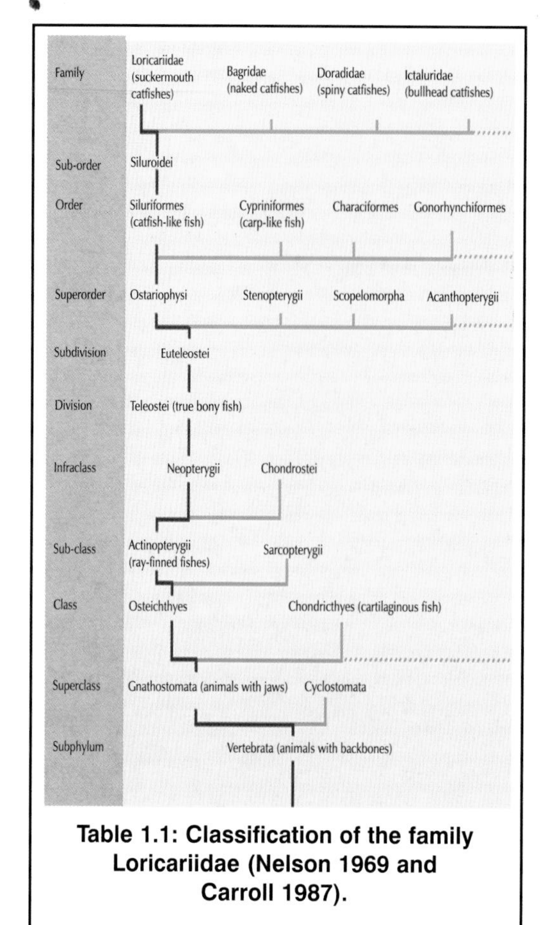

Table 1.1: Classification of the family Loricariidae (Nelson 1969 and Carroll 1987).

All living things that we know about, both those living and extinct species known only from fossils, can be fitted into this pattern of inter-relationships. This is often described as a 'tree'. The trunk represents all living creatures and, as each difference is noted between different groups of creatures, they split into separate 'branches' - each level of which is given a name such as 'order' or 'family'. The final 'twig' is the 'species' level. The entire tree is immense, far too big to draw in a book. Where the lower branches diverge there is little argument and the shape of the tree has been known for a long time. It is obvious, for example, that birds, mammals and reptiles belong on separate branches. However, as the branches split and split again the differences at each split become smaller and smaller and at the final levels there is constant debate. This is why species and genera often move about, confusing the hobbyist with name changes. While one scientist may have decided that a particular characteristic divided different genera, another may later discover characteristics that unite them back into the same branch. New species may be discovered that are so different that a whole new genus needs to be set up just for them, or existing species may be discovered to be closer to the members of another genus than the members of the one they are in.

Table 1.1 shows the start of the branch that will lead to bristlenoses, which are members of the family Loricariidae, along with some of the other branches which diverge at each point. This part of the tree is 'old wood' - new growth is rare and the structure has been established for many years. This is because the differences between the groups are relatively obvious and major.

The order Siluriformes - catfishes

The catfishes (order Siluriformes) are a large and successful order of fish, with around 30 families, 400 genera and over 2,000 species. Today there are species living in both inland and coastal waters of nearly every continent, excluding only the far North and South where the temperatures are too inhospitable. In the past catfish were even more widespread and Eocene fossils were found on Seymour Island, in Antarctica. The earliest known fossil catfish date back to the late Cretaceous.

The family Loricariidae - the suckermouth catfishes

The family Loricariidae are a relatively recent development in catfishes, with no fossil record being known, but they are none the less successful for all that. The *loricariids*, which are widespread through South America, are one of the most prolific catfish families. In 1980 Dr Isbrucker listed some 600 species in his catalogue; now the total is nearer to 1,000 (and growing).They gain their popular name from the modification to their mouths which allows them to hold on in fast flowing water and to efficiently graze over algae beds. Many representatives of the family are commonly seen in aquatic shops. They include the whiptail catfish, the beautiful peckoltias and the 'plecs', as well as bristlenoses. In addition to their mouths, the suckermouth catfish have another obvious modification which has led to them being called 'river armadillos' in some parts of South America. Unlike most fish, catfish have no scales. To replace them, the suckermouth catfish have developed thick bony plates on their skins, known as scutes (meaning 'shield' in Latin).

This group of fish are very popular with aquarists because, in addition to often being very attractive and interesting, they are useful for clearing up algae and food that falls to the bottom of the tank. Some, however are more suitable than others. While bristlenoses are relatively hardy, peaceful, and remain small even when adult, others are not so accommodating. Many species can grow extremely large, exceeding a foot in length. Others can be aggressive or very fussy about exactly the right water conditions. Although many of these fish are fascinating aquarium inhabitants, this book concentrates on bristlenoses as one of the few groups of fish suitable for nearly every aquarist.

Within the family the classifications are highly unstable. New species and new pieces of information are constantly coming to light, largely due to increased accessibility in the Amazon rainforests. Table 1.2 shows the current 'tree' of the close relatives of *Ancistrus* (bristlenoses) in the subfamily Ancistrinae.

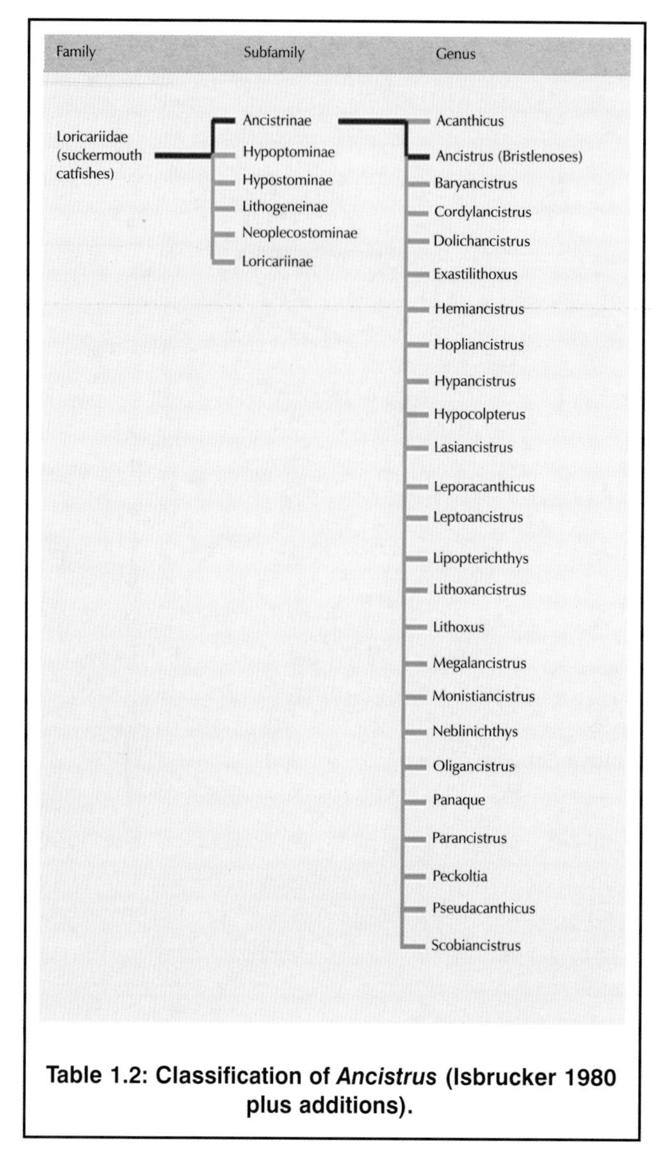

Table 1.2: Classification of *Ancistrus* (Isbrucker 1980 plus additions).

Xenocara and changing classifications

Occasionally bristlenoses are sold in shops under their old genus name of *Xenocara*, and the unwary may be fooled into buying a '*Xenocara* bristlenose' under the impression they are getting something new and unusual. In fact, this name is obsolete; all bristlenoses now belong in the genus *Ancistrus*. Bristlenoses have done more than their fair share of moving around.

Although this may seem arbitrary, each name change is prompted by new information. Although the bristlenoses have stayed in the *Ancistrus* genus for a while now, research into classification has not stopped. At the University of Geneva, investigation is continuing into the genetic structure of the *loricariids*. This research, which is possible for modern scientists because of advances in technology, is likely to produce some new movement in the Loricariidae. Preliminary findings show the *Ancistrus* to indeed belong in the same genus as each other, and to have a close relationship with *Chaetostoma* species, as in the classification at present. The *Ancistrinae* and *Hypostominae* appear to be more closely related than in the currently accepted classification.

The L-numbers and LDA-numbers

In the past, scientists were the first people into a new area to find new fish because they were the only people daft enough to brave unpleasant, exotic diseases and high costs just to come back with a specimen in a bottle. Having done this, they would take great care to enure that the results were fully documented, measuring and recording every aspect of their fish in minute detail. This is the detail that enables the work of classification to continue and means that a fish can be identified as belonging to a particular species with a reasonable degree of confidence.

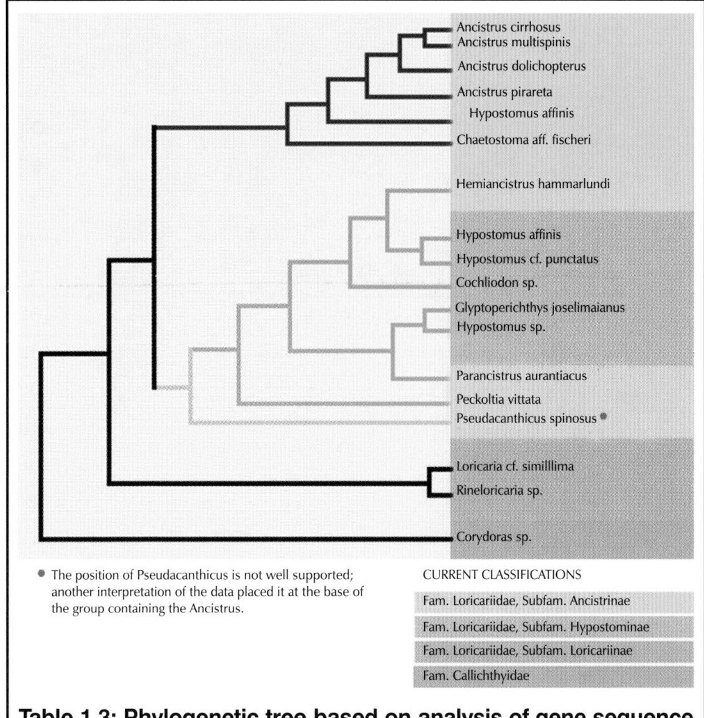

Table 1.3: Phylogenetic tree based on analysis of gene sequence (Montoya-Burgos, Muller, Webster and Pawlowski 1977).

With the advent of cheap and quick air travel it became possible for commercial fish collectors to be first on the scene without waiting for the scientists. A new and exciting array of fish began to flood into the shops at an amazing pace with probable new species appearing almost on a weekly basis. Since these imports were not being properly scientifically documented and named, and hobbyists had no idea what they were buying or where it came from, the L (for *loricariid*) number series was started by the German magazine *Datz.* As each new fish was noticed, it received its fifteen minutes of fame in *Datz* with a photograph and some text. This should have been an excellent idea, with commercial interests behaving responsibly and making public as much information as possible about the new fish.

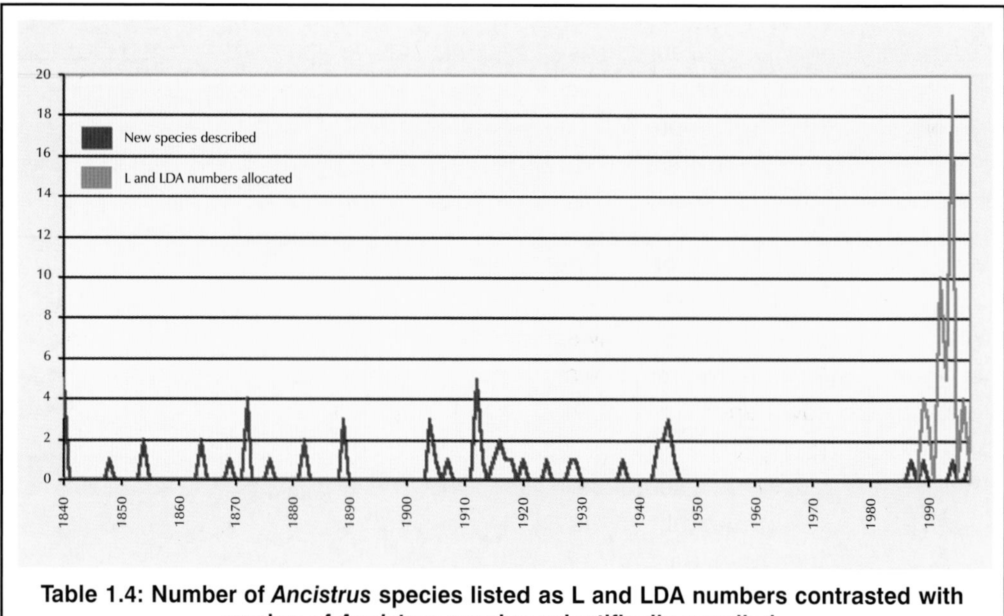

Table 1.4: Number of *Ancistrus* species listed as L and LDA numbers contrasted with number of *Ancistrus* species scientifically supplied.

Unfortunately, commercial considerations rapidly overtook any altruism. Most of the first fish were imported by Transfish (from Planegg near Munich) but other importers were also able to send their photos and descriptions to *Datz* for inclusion in the series. Soon, however, the other importers found that they were having difficulty getting numbers, while Transfish would assign a new L-number to a fish and sell it under that number before publication. This resulted in numbers being allocated to more than one species and, occasionally, to one species ending up with more than one number. To dispel the confusion (!) another German magazine, *Das Aquarium*, started the LDA number series. These are also *loricariids*; some also feature in the L-numbers (but not with the same number) but many are unique to one series or the other.

The L and LDA number series, in addition to being hopelessly confused, are fundamentally flawed because fish cannot be reliably identified from a single photograph of one individual. Furthermore, publications intended to show the all the L-number photographs actually printed some of the wrong photographs for the numbers. As the fish travel straight from the rivers to the retailer, with only a passing stop at the photographers, proper scientific description has been brought almost to a standstill. The table shows the number of *Ancistrus* species that have received only L or LDA numbers against those which have been correctly described; there have been remarkably few of the latter at the very time when there is an explosion of new species which need attention. Although the hobbyist might perceive this bonanza as a good thing, the problems will rapidly become clear when precise identification is required (for example when finding a mate for breeding or when seeking advice). While the colour patterns may seem quite distinctive, many related species of fish share markings that are very similar.

Identifying characteristics of the bristlenose

There are a great many close relatives of the bristlenoses and, often, they are confused by sellers as well as aquarists. Many shops still label everything as 'plecs' (from the time when the only *loricariids* commonly available were *Hypostomus plecostomus*. The fact that there are now hundreds of species appearing in aquatic shops appears to have escaped their notice). Others simply label fish erroneously, which often occurs because the fish were actually imported under the wrong name. On other occasions a batch of little fish may contain several species of several genera which were all caught together and now have been grouped together under one name.

Although all the *loricariids* are interesting, it is quite important to have a rough idea what you are buying. As mentioned before, some groups may grow very large or be very specific in their requirements. Separating bristlenoses from their relatives without dissection is an art which requires practice, but there are several pointers that you can look for.

- The most obvious of these is the presence of bristles! These are the fleshy tentacles which adorn the upper lip and top of the nose in adult males. No other genus of fish exhibits this characteristic. The closest imitation is in *Neblinichthys*, where the males also grow bristles on their heads. However, *Neblinichthys* are not only unlikely to show up in your local retailer but the bristles are entirely different. *Ancistrus* bristles are soft and sensitive, while those of *Neblinichthys* are straight and point stiffly forwards, giving the fish the appearance of a well-used toothbrush. When a male *Ancistrus* is lifted out of the water, the bristles 'disappear'; they are incapable of supporting their own weight in air. Unfortunately, the bristles often only appear on males and, even then, they need to be about an inch and a half long before even tiny bristles are present. This is not much help if the fish you need to identify is female or very young.
- *Ancistrus* also have evertible interopercular spines. These are described more fully in the chapter 'Biology of the Bristlenose'. They appear as a little 'bush' either side of the head when the fish is upset (when being netted, for example). The spines are tipped

with minute hooks, which can make it extremely difficult to extract upset bristlenoses from a net. The picture shows a bristlenose, not unnaturally upset at being out of water. The interopercular spines are visible on the left side of the fish. The hard bony scutes making up the skin are also obvious in this picture; in water they are often not so distinct.

- If the fish can be persuaded to attach itself to the front glass, you will be able to see the stomach (which is bare and has no armour-plating) as well as

Figure 1.1: The soft bristles collapse out of water.

Figure 1.2: *Ancistrus* sp. showing interopercular spines everted.

Figure 1.3: The sharp, hooked spines, coupled with locking mechanisms in the fins, can make it difficult to extract the fish from the net.

the shape of the fish and its mouth. Since most shops are unwilling to let you catch the fish and upset them to see if they have interopercular spines, the shape is the most useful way of identifying the fish in an aquarium shop. When you first start looking at the *loricariids*, they all look very similar. However, the more you look at, the more easily you will be able to tell the difference - practice makes perfect!

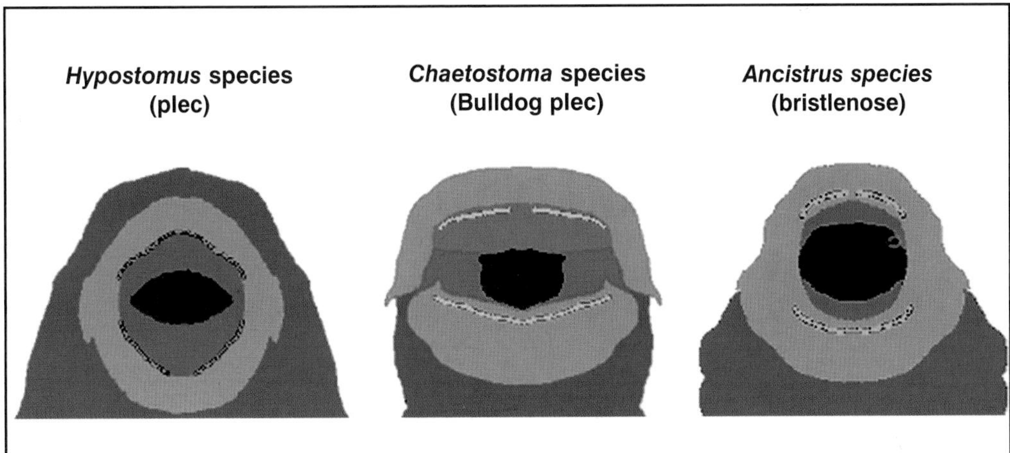

Figure 1.4: Mouth formation of commonly available *loricariid* species.

- The picture shows the mouths of some of the commonly available *loricariid* species. Although all have mouths adapted into flat 'suckers' there is a considerable difference in shape of both the mouth and the head.
- Just as the mouth shapes vary between different genera, the body shapes, too, are distinctive. The picture shows three common *loricariid* species overlaid, showing the

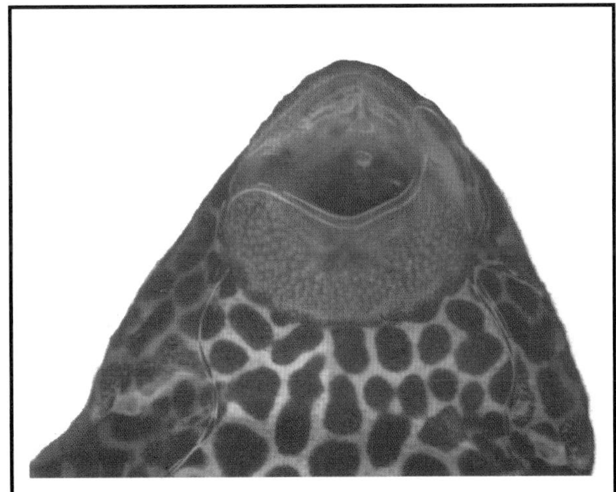

Figure 1.5: Mouth of *Glyptoperichthys gibbiceps* (red plec).

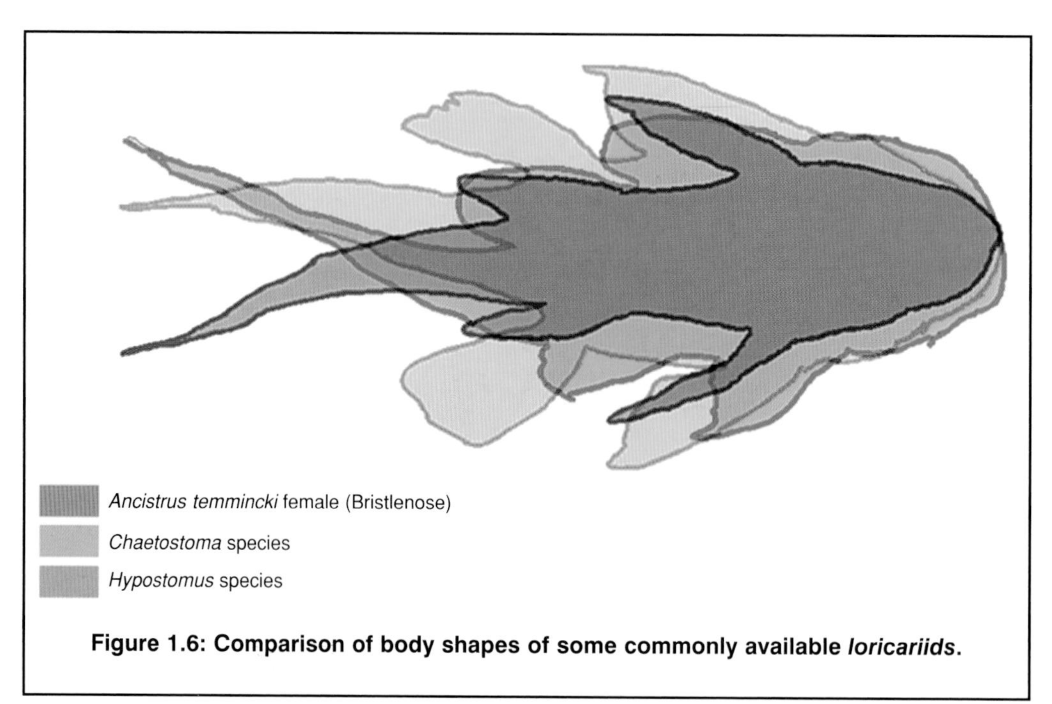

Figure 1.6: Comparison of body shapes of some commonly available *loricariids*.

Figure 1.7: Ventral view of *Chaetostoma* species.

characteristic shapes of each. The bristlenose can be seen to be broad at the shoulders (pectoral fins) with the head narrowing in a triangular shape towards the nose. The entire body is comparatively stocky when compared to the much thinner *Hypostomus*, and the *Chaetostoma* which is as broad at the nose as at the pectoral fins.

Figure 1.9: *Glyptoperichthys* species, ventral view.

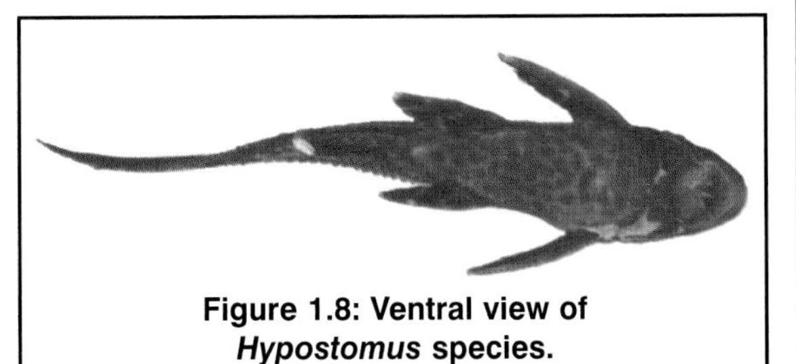

Figure 1.8: Ventral view of *Hypostomus* species.

Figure 1.10: LDA8, gold marble *Ancistrus*, ventral view.

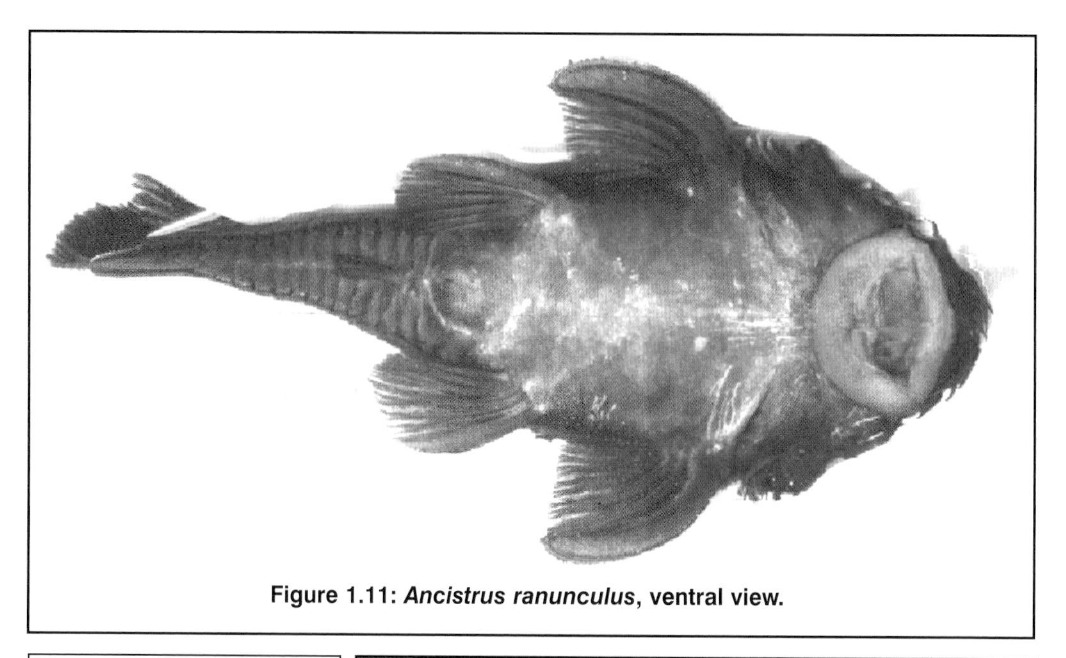

Figure 1.11: *Ancistrus ranunculus*, ventral view.

Figure 1.12: *Ancistrus* species, ventral view.

Figure 1.13: This baby 'bristlenose' on sale isn't an *Ancistrus* at all.

Biology of the Bristlenose 2

Although the bristlenose may seem a strange and exotic fish to our eyes, it is actually ideally suited to its environment with a strange and wonderful set of adaptations that make *Ancistrus* not only a successful group of fish but resilient and adaptable too.

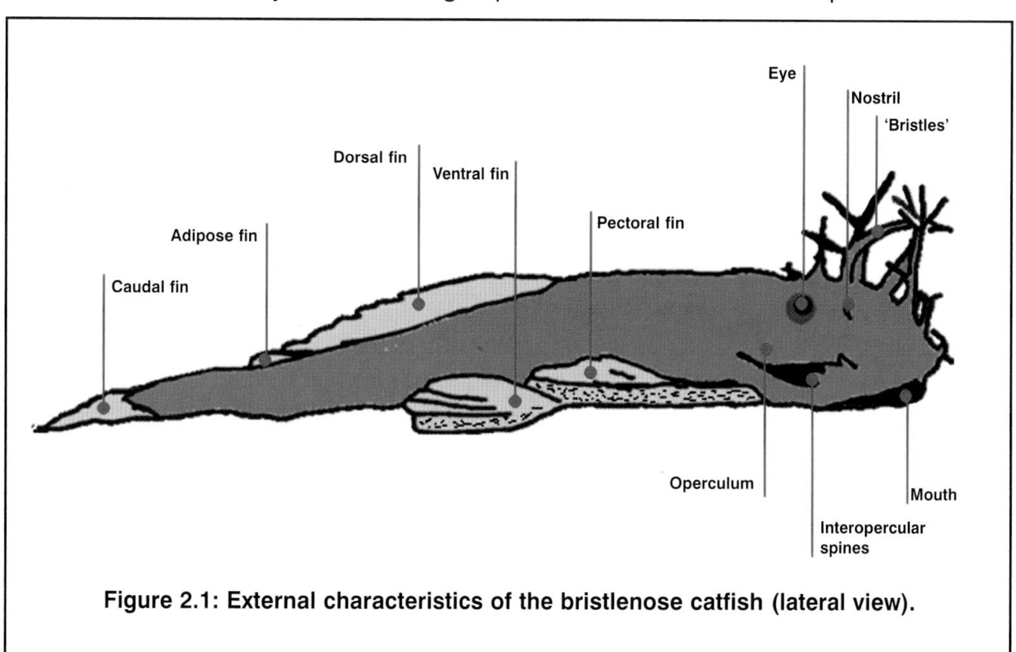

Figure 2.1: External characteristics of the bristlenose catfish (lateral view).

Sensing the world around

Mother Nature is not often the kind and benevolent entity we would like to think, especially for the little individuals who depend on her largess. Romantic concepts have little place in the lives of bristlenoses whose every day is an unremitting effort to find enough to eat, to avoid being eaten, and to reproduce. In the pursuit of these three aims acute senses are essential to success. Fortunately the bristlenoses are well supplied with these.

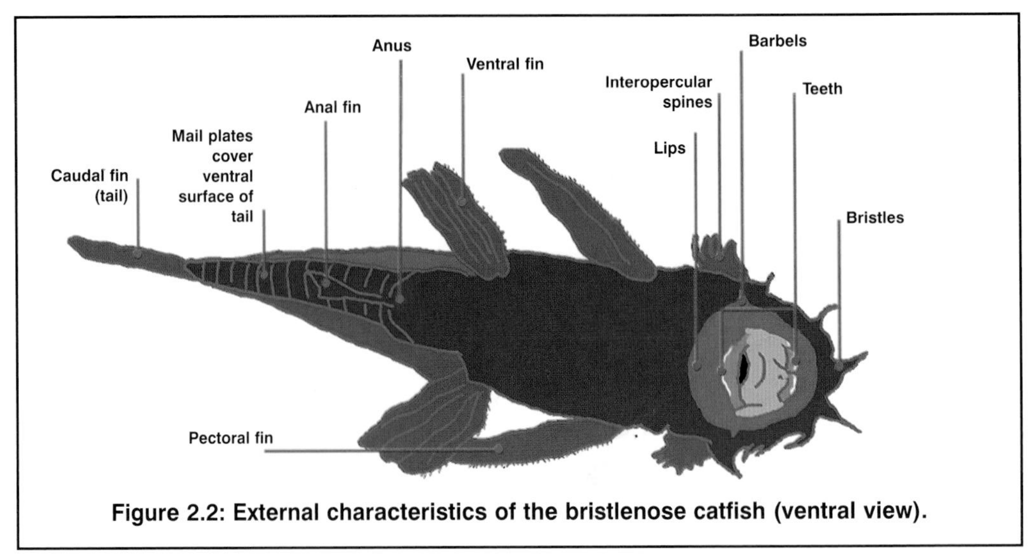

Figure 2.2: External characteristics of the bristlenose catfish (ventral view).

The eyes of bristlenoses, and the Loricariidae family generally, are equipped with a papillary iris flap. Just as in humans, this can expand to cut out light when they are exposed to bright lights or contract to allow the maximum available light to reach the eye when conditions are darker. No other family of fish has this unique eye formation, although some flatfishes have a similar mechanism. The flap can clearly be seen in aquarium fishes as a small gold horseshoe at the top of the eye.

Figure 2.3: The iris flap can clearly be seen at the top of the eye in this male.

Figure 2.4: Eye of *Glyptoperichthys* species.

The eyes of the bristlenose, however, are of limited importance. Often they live in rivers of low visibility, on rocky or woody substrates where the line of sight may be severely limited. Furthermore, the eyes are firmly situated on top of the head, looking up into the water, while the fish must find food on the substrate below it and successfully manoeuvre its mouth to the correct position. Fortunately, other senses come to the rescue to compensate for this.

Loricariids have, like many other catfish, a reduced swim bladder. This organ serves to regulate the buoyancy of fish that have more traditional lifestyles, making sure that they don't bob to the surface or sink like stones. *Loricariids*, however, actually want to sink. They spend their entire lives on the substrate or, possibly, clinging to rocks or wood with their powerful sucking mouths. They certainly have very little interest in swimming and don't need to regulate their position in the water. In spite of this, the swim bladder is not only present but strongly protected by fused and flattened vertebrae which are not only fused to each other but also to the skull. Underneath this shelter the swim bladder consists of two atrophied lobes, one either side of the body, connected by a narrow channel.

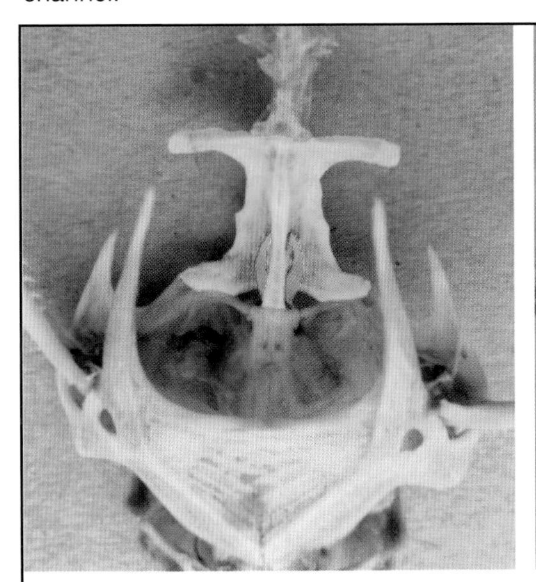

Figure 2.5: Ventral view of skeleton showing fused upper vertebrae protecting the swim bladder and tripus (green tint).

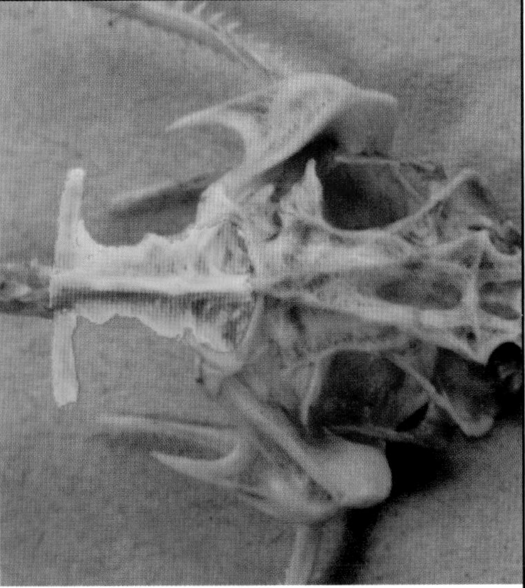

Figure 2.6: Dorsal view of fused vertebrae which, as can be seen, are fused to the skull bones.

The swim bladder serves the fish for another purpose rather than buoyancy. Most catfish own four extra paired bones which, together, are called the Weberian apparatus. This sequence of bones - from the inner ear (sinus impar) to the swim bladder - consists of: the claustrum, scaphium, intercalarium and tripus, which finally joins on to the swim bladder with projections. In bristlenoses, the Weberian apparatus consists of only two ossicles, or small bones, the scaphium and the tripus. These are connected by thick fibrous connective tissue. When the swim bladder vibrates with noises in the water, the bones also vibrate and the sound is transferred to the inner ear. As the thick muscly body wall would impair sound, there is a patch on each side of the body, beside the swim bladder, where there is no muscle; here only fat and skin separates the swim bladder from the outside world. This muscle-free patch is one of the differences which separate the catfish from the cyprinids, which also have Weberian ossicles. Catfish are not supposed to be able to understand which direction the sounds are coming from when they are heard by the swim bladder, as both sides meet up in a common chamber before the sounds are transmitted to the ear.

The lateral line is a line of sensory organs running down the side of the body. In *Ancistrus* the head lateral line nerve runs extremely close to the inner ear and is separated from it only by a thin membrane. Furthermore, the front part of the body lateral line runs inside the bony protection next to the swim bladder. Since the function of the lateral line is to translate pressure waves in the water into information about its surroundings for the fish, it seems likely that sounds transmitted through the ear and swim bladder could stimulate the lateral line nerves to supply even more information to the fish. As there are corresponding lateral line nerves on each side of the body, the fish could use this to overcome the problem of not knowing the direction of swim-bladder detected sounds.

The swim bladder may be used in the production of sound; distressed bristlenoses can emit a high-pitched aggrieved squeak. The sounds come from rotating the pectoral spines in the sockets; the noise is then amplified by the swim bladder. I have only heard this sound twice, both times when extracting an irate bristlenose from a plantpot hole that I was sure was far too small for him to get into. Normal catching and treatment of the fish does not produce the same enraged effects. In addition to supercharged hearing, the bristlenoses also have a highly developed sense of taste. Unlike humans, who only have tastebuds in their mouths, many catfish are covered from head to tail in taste buds. The sensitive bristles of the males are particular rich in these sensory structures.

Although the entire skin is a sensory organ for tasting the water and assisting in the location of food, the mouth is even more sensitive. The whole surface of the lips is covered with taste buds but the fleshy papillae that give the lips a granulated look are particularly rich in sensory buds.

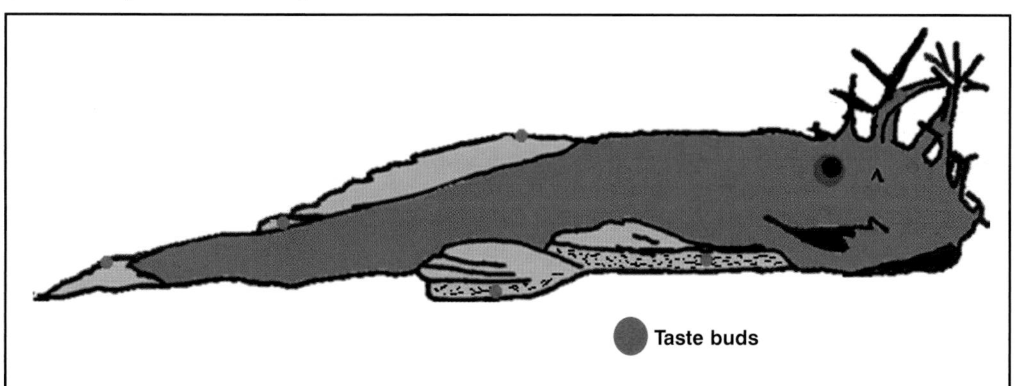

Figure 2.7: Location of taste buds noted on a bristlenose catfish (R Dana Ono 1980) - the buds are located symmetrically on both sides of the body.

Not content with a plethora of taste buds, *Ancistrus* species also have another form of sensory receptors towards the front of the lower body. These appear similar to structures in the lateral line but, as yet, we do not know their function.

The usefulness of senses other than sight is exemplified by the existence of three species of troglodyte bristlenoses whose eyes are useless in the dark of the caves. Like many blind cave fish, their eyes become covered over with skin as they grow.

The sucker mouth

The flat sucker mouth of the bristlenose is perfectly adapted to a life grazing algae from a rocky or woody substrate. The flat mouth is situated under the body where it will naturally come into contact with the food. In addition to powerfully grinding teeth which can rasp away all but the toughest algae (and indeed solid wood), the mouth serves to anchor the fish in place. This suction is so strong that to wrench a fish free from its hold could damage it. Unfortunately the fish have to breathe at the same time as holding on. Fish breathe by taking water in through the mouth and passing it out through the gills, over the blood-rich gill filaments which absorb oxygen. Small grooves near the barbels allow water to enter even while the fish is sucking on to a flat substrate. This is a modification not shared by other fish with a sucking mouth, such as *Gyrinocheilus*, the sucking loach. It must breath both in and out through its gills. Along with its flattened body shape, which reduces resistance to the water current, the sucker mouth makes the fish perfectly designed for life in fast currents.

In addition to bearing taste buds, holding the fish in place and grinding algae, the sucker mouth has another modification for some *loricariids*. The papillae on the lips are not only armed with taste buds, but with tiny groups of brushes. These formations grow in a patch in front of the taste buds. It may be surmised that in some way they protect the taste buds from damage by sweeping away particles and they possibly serve to break up food, releasing the flavours ready for the taste buds. The brushes were not found in some of the other *loricariids* tested; although *Ancistrus Chaetostoma*, *Hypostomus* and *Farlowella* species proved to have the brushes, *Loricaria* and *Otocinclus* species did not. It was concluded that those fish who lived on rocky or woody, firm, substrates had brushes whereas those that spent more time swimming or on muddy substrates did not.

The main bones which form the mouth can be seen in figure 2.9. This shows an

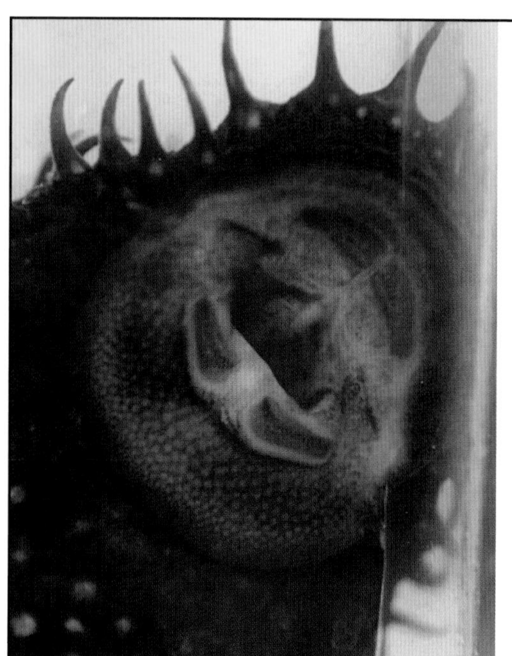

Figure 2.8: The oral papillae are easily seen on the lips of this *Ancistrus*.

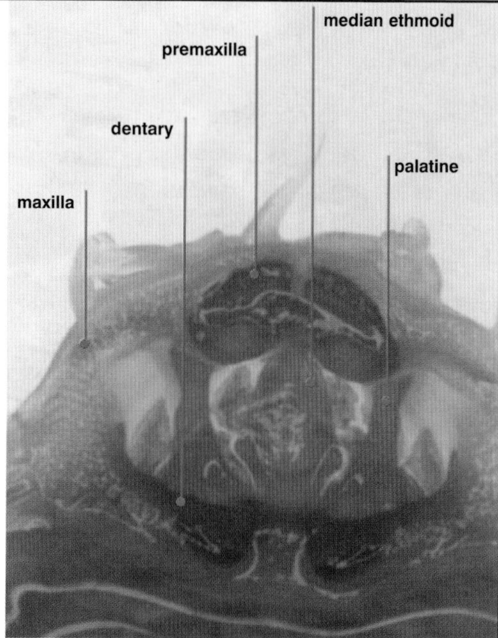

Figure 2.9: The main bones of the mouth (ventral view).

alizarin preparation of an *Ancistrus ranunculus*. This is a treatment whereby the flesh of the preserved fish becomes transparent and the bones are stained red so that they can be seen in position within the body of the fish. The maxilla bones move to erect and relax the back and sides of the lips. The teeth are only on the premaxillae and the dentary and are small and numerous. Each is divided into two lobes, although you would need a very good magnifying glass to see this.

Breathing

Although bristlenoses prefer lots of oxygen, they often find themselves stranded in dry-season pools with no current and a long wait before the rains will liberate them again. To counteract the ill-effects of this, they are able to breathe atmospheric air using their intestines as a 'lung'.

An investigation by L. Satora using *Ancistrus multispinis* showed that within the long intestine is an area rich in capillaries. The thin walls of the capillaries are able to absorb oxygen from swallowed air in the intestine. This part of the intestine has few gastric glands, and no mucous producing cells; the surface of the intestine is made of a tissue called 'simple squamous epithelium', which is typically found where gas diffusion occurs. Special structures known as lamellar bodies were also found in the surface which may produce chemicals similar to those produced in mammalian lungs which facilitate the absorption of oxygen. Such structures had not been found in the stomachs of any other fish at the time of the experiment (1998). All the individuals examined had air both in their stomachs and intestines.

In addition to having a stomach that can help them breathe, the longer that bristlenoses live in reduced oxygen, the better they actually get at it. In an experiment in 1982 the frequency of taking gulps of atmospheric air was noted for *Ancistrus chagresi*. As the experiment went on, the fish needed to gulp oxygen less often in spite of low oxygenation conditions persisting in the water. Once acclimated, they have a higher concentration of haemoglobin (the 'red' colour in blood, which carries oxygen around the body), are able to take in up to 25% more at a gasp than non-acclimated fish, and can hold each breath longer.

When breathing, it is not only necessary to take oxygen into the body but to somehow get rid of the waste carbon dioxide that is created. Since little is discharged from the intestinal route, the carbon dioxide must leave through the gills. This poses a problem because, if the fish continues gill breathing at the same time as it is using oxygen taken from air in the intestine, it risks the hard-won oxygen going out from the gills in a 'reverse breathing' operation back into the oxygen-depleted water. To combat this possibility, it increases its gill breathing at the same time as the last gasp of air is nearly finished. The blood is then low in oxygen, so there is little to be lost to the water and the carbon dioxide can be excreted. This done, it can then take another gasp of air.

This ability to breathe air probably accounts for the fact that these fast-water fish were already spawning in home aquaria when aeration and filtration was regarded by some authors as a luxury. This is not, however, any sort of excuse to keep your long-suffering fish in conditions where it has to adjust its metabolism to survive. The fish will do even better in conditions to their liking! From personal observation, it may be that very young bristlenoses do not yet have the mechanism for air breathing properly developed; in low-oxygen conditions they start to suffer very quickly and fatalities are almost certain.

Skin and skeleton

These may seem like vastly different topics but, in the mailed *loricariids*, the skin and skeleton can be regarded as being the same thing. The protective scutes that cover the body are constructed of bone. The entire skeleton and armour constitutes a large percentage of the fish. When the skeleton of a *Hypostomus plecostomus* was weighed, it was found to constitute 13% of the entire body weight. This can be contrasted against between 5.5% and 7.1% for various cyprinids. The effect of this massive armour is to make the fish well-protected against most of the dangers it is likely to encounter underwater. When Mary Power was investigating the depths at which different *loricariids* hunted for food, she noticed several specimens which were going blind and seemed to her to be easy to catch. Nonetheless, these fish turned up regularly in the counts and showed no signs of being picked off by predators. Indeed, bristlenoses have a number of adaptations that make them a singularly unappetising meal for a hungry fish.

First among these are the locking fin rays. The first fin ray of each fin is thickened and often ornamented with an array of odontodes. These are bony 'thorns' or teeth. When the fish is threatened, the pectoral, ventral and adipose fins can be locked into an erect position by an extremely clever mechanism. This serves several purposes: it makes the fish look bigger; it can help to wedge the fish irremovably in a secure crevice; and, if all else fails, it can make clear to a predator that the meal will be at the cost of a severely scratched throat! This mechanism ensures that the fins cannot be forced down without breaking them and can be observed working in skeletons of dead fish.

These rays require a solid structure behind to support them; there is no use in erecting a strong fence in shallow sand so the locking spines are supported by a strong

Figure 2.10: The first rays of the fin are strong and thickened.

Figure 2.11: In close-up, the fin spine can be seen to be roughened with hundreds of thorny odontodes.

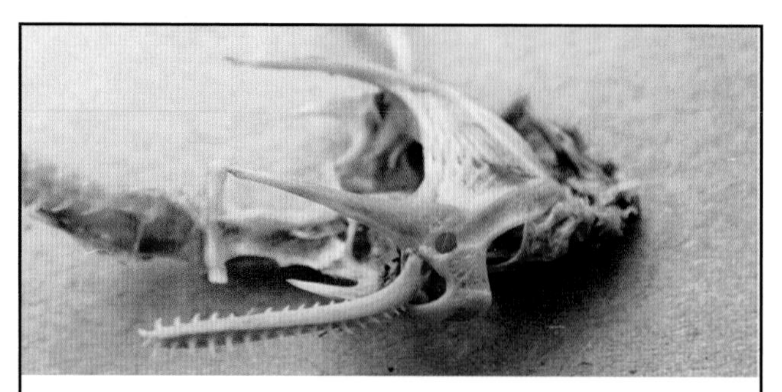

Figure 2.12: The odontode 'teeth' on the thickened pectoral fin ray can clearly be seen in this photograph, as well as the joint where the locking mechanism controls the fin ray. This fin is in the erect position.

Figure 2.13: The massive formation of the skull and fused pectoral girdle form a strong foundation for the locking pectoral fins.

bone structure. The pectoral girdle, with the massive coracoid and cleithrum bones, is fused to, and inseparable from, the strong skull.

In addition to the spiny, sharp fin rays, the fish has another set of offensive spines: the interopercular spines. These are attached to a partially ossified ligament, joining the operculum and interoperculum and when the operculum is raised by the dilatator operculi muscle, the interopercular ligament and its spines are pulled upward and outward. The interoperculum and the preoperculum are immovably fused together. The preoperculum, in turn, is fused to the bones of the skull. The numbers and shape of the spines varies between species and is often used as one of the identifying characteristics for them. The spines are hooked, and usually include a clump of large ones plus some smaller ones. They are very sharp and careless aquarists can find that puncture wounds from these itch unpleasantly.

If a predator should succeed in swallowing a bristlenose, it is likely to end up with a severe case of indigestion. The back and sides of the fish are encased in thick bony scutes, each of which is further ornamented by tiny odontodes. These make the fish look

Figure 2.14: In this *Ancistrus ranunculus* specimen, the interopercular spines are fully extended, showing their sharp hooked tips.

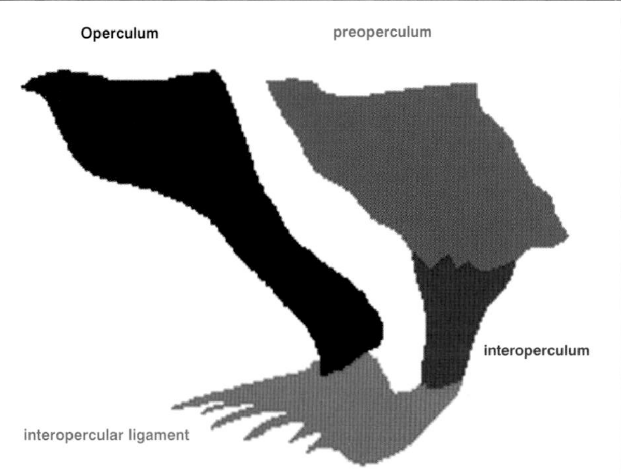

Figure 2.15: Movements of the operculum pull the ligament up and out, erecting the spines.

furry in some lights and, if you stroke a bristlenose gently, you will feel the odontodes - the fish feels like sandpaper.

The only vulnerable part of the fish is the soft, unprotected ventral surface. Since that is invariably pressed firmly against the substrate or some other flat surface, it is unlikely to cause the fish too much of a problem.

The scutes are larger and heavier than ordinary fish scales and the bristlenose must pay the price in mobility for safety. Whereas normal fish can bend sinuously through currents, the bristlenose is considerably more unwieldy and swimming is very laborious. No bristlenose could remain in midwater if it wanted to. Rather, their swimming endeavours consist more of propelling themselves across flat surfaces with thrusts from their fins and grabbing hold again before gravity wins. It is physically impossible for them to bend very far in any direction. This method of locomotion may not sound very practical, but anyone who has pursued a bristlenose determined to elude capture can testify that they are very good at it and can slide across the glass at a remarkable rate.

The skin serves for protection in more ways than one. In addition to being a coat of armour, it also acts as an invisible cloak. The usual patterns for bristlenoses feature a background of anything between pale brown and black, usually with a liberal patterning of pale spots, squiggles or patches. While a jet black fish with white dots may appear unlikely to fade into the background anywhere, as soon as it is under a piece of bogwood

Figure 2.16: Bristlenoses can blend in with their surroundings.

Figure 2.17: See below.

Figure 2.18: The same fish as 2.17, exhibiting different colours.

it vanishes. The uneven patterns simulate the play of light and dark on variable substrates extremely well. To add to a basic camouflage colour form, they also have chameleon like qualities. If you place your bristlenose on tartan you won't get a remarkable result, but you can observe them changing colour, often relatively dramatically, in the aquarium. Colour changes depend on a variety of factors - lighting, substrate colour and, often, simply the fish's mood at the time.

The two fish in figures 2.17 and 2.18 appear totally different. I have seen photos of fish that could be siblings to 2.17 identified as *A. dolichopterus* while the fish in 2.18 is quite plainly a '*hoplogenys*-type' species. Unfortunately for this identification they are actually the same fish, adapting himself to different circumstances and different days.

Sexual differences

Bristlenoses are 'sexually dimorphic'; that is, there are secondary sexual characteristics which mean that the aquarist can easily tell one from the other. The most obvious of these are the soft bristles, which start to develop early, at about an inch and a half. Since there are species in which the females also have bristles, or you may wish to sex juvenile fish, it is fortunate that there are other differences.

The male is a larger fish - not just longer, where the difference is only slight, but he is also much chunkier too. This is particularly obvious across the pectoral fins, where the difference is immediately apparent, especially if the fish are looked at from the bottom.

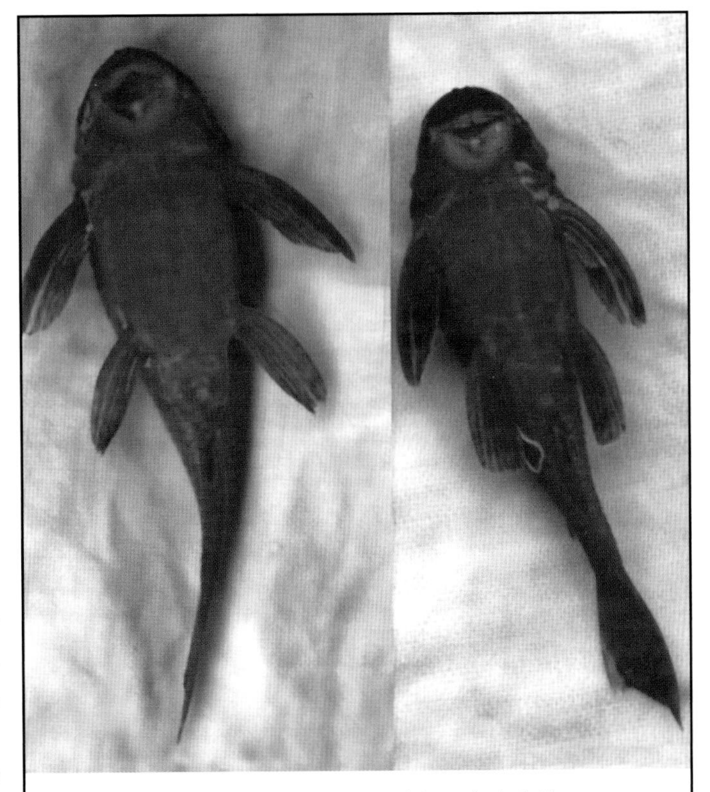

Figure 2.20: Juvenile male and female bristlenoses. The male is on the right.

In figure 2.20 two juvenile bristlenoses are shown. The fish on the right was in fact smaller than the left fish, although the photos have been adjusted to show them closer to the same size to emphasise the differences. The smaller fish, which has since grown a good set of bristles, can be seen to be a good deal thicker in proportion, especially around the head where the tissue has started to thicken where the bristles will grow. In adult fish the differences are even more apparent. In fish that are known to be of the same age, the males start to become larger very quickly. Where there is a small and a large fish that are siblings, the larger is almost invariably a male and the smaller a female.

In species where both male and female develop bristles, the bristles are more plentiful and prominent on the males. This is apparent in Figure 2.21 in which the female, although well equipped with a good bush of bristles, can be seen to be nowhere near as

Figure 2.21: Male and female *Ancistrus ranunculus*. The female is on the right.

Figure 2.22: Not only do the bristles help to identify males but their positioning on the upper lip and snout can help to differentiate species.

well adorned as the male. His bristles are not only longer, but extra rows can be seen further up the nose. In addition, the interopercular spines of males are far larger than those of the equivalent females.

Bristlenoses at home 3

Bristlenose country

Bristlenoses occupy most of South America with their range reaching down as far as Argentina. Specimens (probably ex-aquarium) have been introduced in Central America and can be found as far North as Florida. At least two species are found in Oahu, Hawaii, and populate many reservoirs so extensively that it is suggested they are a major threat to indigenous species.

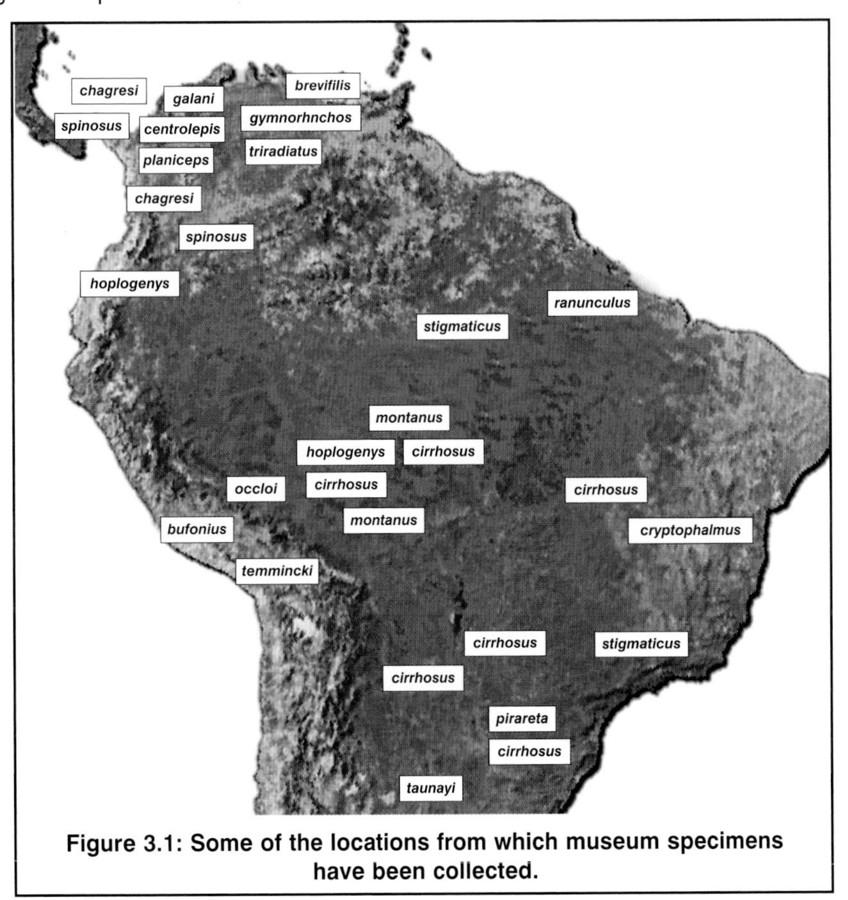

Figure 3.1: Some of the locations from which museum specimens have been collected.

The map (figure 3.1) shows the locations where some of the specimens in museums were collected, which demonstrates the wide spread of the fish. Although the map is certainly not exhaustive (because there is not enough room to show all the specimens ever collected), it can be seen that some species occur in a relatively large number of geographically separated locations; *Ancistrus cirrhosus* is the best example of this. By comparison, *Ancistrus ranunculus* is only known from the Xingu and Tocantins river systems. This is of relevance to the aquarist in that a species that has been able to colonise a large area is likely to be more adaptable to new conditions. Although there is always some doubt about the identification of specimens, there is no doubt that *cirrhosus* is a resilient and adaptable fish. For a more exhaustive list of species and their habitats, see Appendix 1. *Ancistrus cirrhosus* and *dolichopterus* have even been found in brackish waters.

South America is not a small continent and the river systems are proportionately massive. Although aquarists tend to think of South America as one entity and habitat, the area the bristlenoses inhabit covers about 14,297,178 square kilometres - about sixty times the size of the United Kingdom - while the Amazon river alone is 6,437 kilometres long. This does not include its massive tributaries or the other river systems which bristlenoses also inhabit. The range of habitats in other river systems is, however, similar to those encompassed by the Amazon network, with low-lying rainforests fed by rivers rising in high mountainous areas. Bristlenoses that live in other river systems are thus exposed to a similar range of conditions.

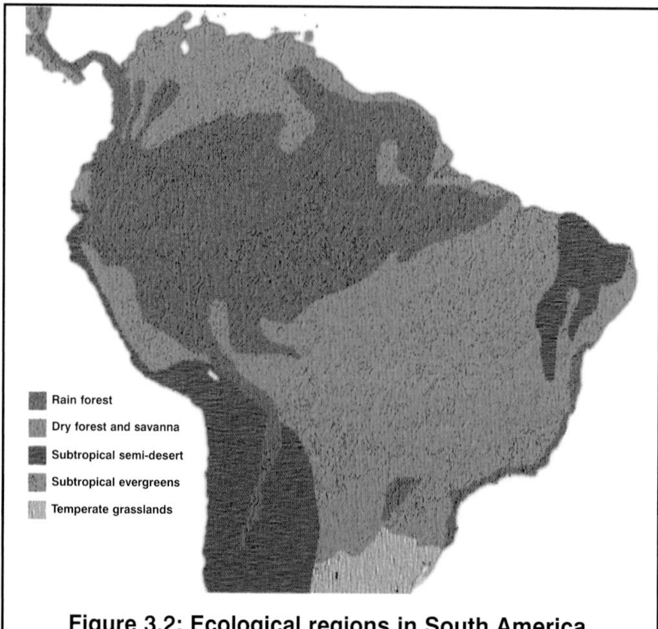

Figure 3.2: Ecological regions in South America.

The ecological conditions range from the rainforests to relatively arid areas. Figure 3.2 shows the

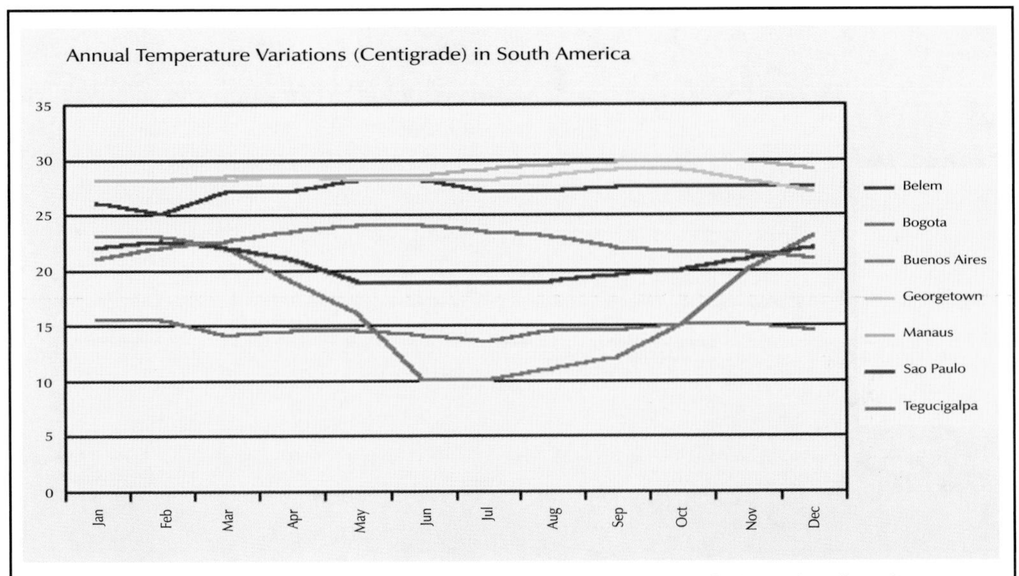

Table 3.1: Temperature changes throughout the year in S. America (London Geographical Institute 1948). See Fig 5.1 for a key to the places mentioned.

various ecological regions of South America.

Although temperatures are high and relatively stable in the rainforests, South America also includes the snow-capped Andes and other highlands where temperatures can be considerably cooler. The Rio Xingu, in the heart of the rainforest, can exceed 90°F while other areas where the bristlenoses are found can fall below 70°F. The temperature varies little in the rainforest but, in other habitats, seasonal variations can be seen.

Waters in the Amazon network belong to three types: blackwater,

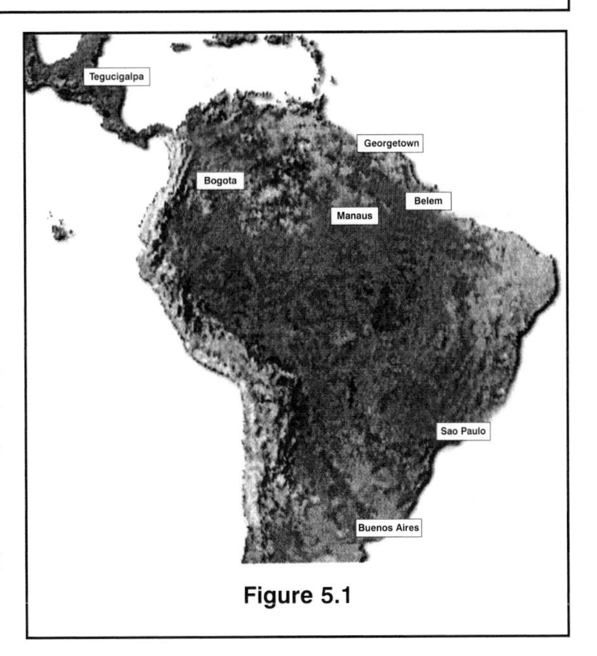

Figure 5.1

whitewater and clearwater, each of which has different properties. Blackwater, such as the Rio Negro, is the colour of tea and is very acidic, with almost non-existent hardness. The colour and the acidity stem from where the river rises in shallow sandy soils colonised by shrubby plants. Here humic acids leach into the river, staining it the characteristic colour. Blackwater is poor in nutrients and supports little in the way of plant life.

Whitewater, such as is found in the Rio Branco and Napo, is the colour of milky coffee. These rivers flow across easily erodable soils, where they collect a high load of sediment. These rivers are nutritious and various aquatic plants, both rooted and floating, flourish.

Figure 3.3: Netting fish in the Rio Xingu. Photo: Harald Schultz

Figure 3.4: Vegetation and algae in the Upper Xingu. Photo: Harald Schultz

Clearwaters, such as the Rio Xingu, flow across ancient rocks from which any nutrients and soft parts have long since been scoured away. They are, therefore, poor in nutrients and low in sediment; few plants are supported by these rivers.

The rivers and their systems also encompass a variety of habitats, from the often anoxic (without oxygen) depths of the main rivers to little streams. Isolated pools are formed as the waters recede in the dry season, while the rains cause massive rises in the water level of most rivers, inundating huge areas of forest. By preference, bristlenoses prefer fast flowing streams and small rivers. They can also be found in isolated, current-free pools, at the edges of the main rivers, and in the small waterways between the islands in river archipelagos. There are even three species (so far) that inhabit the perpetual night of deep cave systems.

The changing seasons

The lives of many South American fish are governed by the rains and the following dry season. Although temperature variation is minimal over much of their distribution, the

Figure 3.5: The South American network of rivers.

Figure 3.6: Islands in the rivers provide extra habitats for bristlenoses.
Photo: Harald Schultz

Figure 3.8: *Ancistrus* prefer shallower tributaries with good algae growth........
Photo: Dr D Sands

Figure 3.9:.......to the spartan depths of major rivers (Rio Purus).

Figure 3.10: Dry season in the Takatu river with sandbars showing. *Ancistrus* can become trapped in isolated pools when the water level is low.
Photo: Dr D Sands

importance of the increased territory brought by floodwaters is crucial. Most rivers go through large changes in water level, although some streams remain at a more or less constant level all year. The floodplains of the Amazon and its main tributaries covers about 300,000 km^2 and smaller tributaries and rivers account for another 1 million km^2. As the water rises over the floodplains, nutrients in the soils and from organic matter enters the water. Throughout the river network, algae and plankton communities prosper from the influx of nutrients carried down from above. The floodplains are now open to the bristlenoses and those that were trapped in pools when the waters receded have an opportunity to escape.

Flooding levels can vary from year to year. The depth is also controlled by the point in the river; higher up, fewer tributaries swell the waters, whereas in the lower reaches a large river may have accumulated the flood waters of many smaller ones. Table 3.2 shows the maximum level reached by Rio Negro waters over a period of two years, both in the upper and lower reaches.

Feeding and behaviour

Although rises in the water level may make terrestrial plants accessible to the hungry *Ancistrus*, these do not appear to play any part in their diet. Rather, the advantages are in the

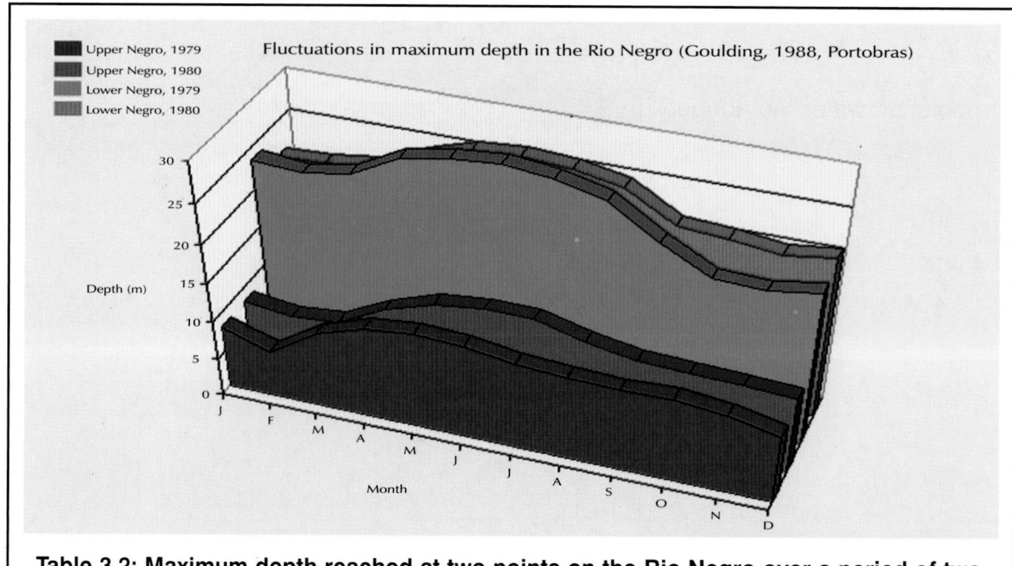

Table 3.2: Maximum depth reached at two points on the Rio Negro over a period of two years (Goulding 1988 from data provided by Portobras, Manaus).

increased availability of algae. As algae grows thickest where it receives the most light, the most algae is available in the shallows. Unfortunately a number of predators, such as herons, are well aware of this and patrol the shallows looking for unwary fish. The larger bristlenoses remain in the depths where pickings are sparse. The smaller fish, who are less conspicuous and at greater risk from other fish than birds, can graze in the shallows freely. As the water level rises, the shallows are no longer so shallow and the larger fish can graze there safely. Experiments done on this subject by Mary E Power (1984) show that during the dry season the large fish either lost weight or just managed to maintain their weight; in the bonanza provided by the floods the fish rapidly grew. As the rainy season progressed, the fish continued to gain weight but not to the degree of the initial spurt of growth.

Being able to get a good meal is more likely to make fish feel like spawning than slow starvation and, with the increase in food and territory, spawning activity is stimulated. These patterns may be repeated in aquaria by some fish who show seasonal spawning tendencies.

Figure 3.12: The high water marks and tree roots are visible during dry season in the Rio Negro. Photo: Dr D Sands

As the rains slow, the floodwaters recede. In some areas bristlenoses are trapped in pools of water no longer connected to the main river; in these the current is negligible and the fish must struggle by on reduced oxygen.

Figure 3.13: In the wet season large areas of land become a new foraging ground. Photo: Dr D Sands

Although male bristlenoses are reputed to be aggressive and territorial towards each other, bristlenoses are naturally inclined to band together in loose groups. *Ancistrus ranunculus* were even found with several bristlenoses sharing the same

Figure 3.14: Vast volumes of water flow down major Amazon tributaries like the Negro. Photo: Dr D Sands

Figure 3.15: In the upper reaches of the rivers the flow is fast and the water well oxygenated. Photo: Dr D Sands

crevices. Another series of experiments by Mary Power found that fish kept in solitude lost weight faster without food than do those who are allowed to group together, suggesting that they find tangible benefits in company. There certainly appear to be benefits in areas where sedimentation and detritus cover the floor of the river. When the algae is covered by a layer of mud, the bristlenoses must not only waste energy clearing it away, but also use energy in attempting to digest swallowed detritus and trying to breathe in a cloud of grit.

By following paths where other *Ancistrus* have grazed, they can minimise the amount of dirt that they encounter. Little fish show a marked preference for following bigger ones around, as the larger fish can clear sediment that would overwhelm the smaller individuals. This sediment clearance not only allows the fish to reach the algae already growing there but also stimulates new algae to grow. Such patches show new algal growth within twenty-four hours, providing a new clean meal for the next bristlenose who ventures along. On encountering heavy sediment, the fish have been observed to perform a 'head-down wiggle', so that the sediment is disturbed and carried away by the current. It is also suggested by Mary Power that greater numbers of bristlenoses may mitigate the unpleasant effects of sediment by eating it and passing it out into more compact and stable faeces. The next fish to come along will then not find a cloud of mud but neat droppings that can be avoided. Obviously it takes a lot of mud eating to clear a space in this way, but every little helps!

Figure 3.16: The shallow algae beds in this Peruvian stream provide an ideal nursery for young *Ancistrus*. Photo: Dr D Sands

A study of fish in the Rio Negro by Michael Goulding and colleagues reported several species of bristlenose as detritivores ('eating the muck on the bottom') from the contents of their stomachs. It is more reasonable to suppose that these unfortunates were simply forced to eat large volumes of detritus in order to find any algae. Other studies have shown algae as forming the major part of their diet with insect larvae as a secondary food, although all specimens had eaten some mud and sand.

Certainly, in the aquarium, bristlenoses cannot be expected to live off the filth in the bottom of dirty tanks and such an existence would be actively harmful to them. An analysis of the different foods in the stomachs of one group of bristlenoses not only showed a clear preference for algae but also for certain types of algae. Examination of faeces showed that although the bristlenoses would eat lots of different sorts of algae, the tough filamentous algae were passed through more or less intact whereas the softer diatomaceous algae were digested successfully.

Although insect larvae form only a comparatively small part of the diet, they are nonetheless eaten with relish when they can be found. One group of midge larvae has learnt to keep out of the way by making a home on the bristlenose itself, as well as on other *loricariids*, well out of the way of the hungry mouth. The interopercular spines are a favourite retreat and the larvae can settle there, feeding on disturbed detritus and protected by the spines from the attentions of other fish. They live their lives and pupate without leaving their ambulatory home.

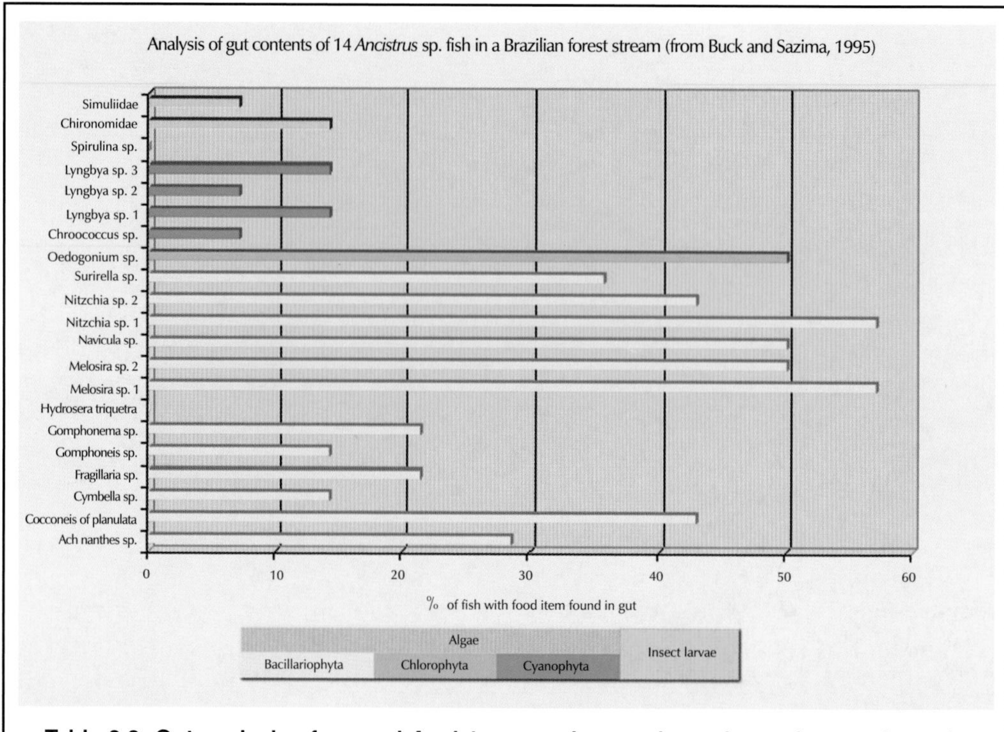

Table 3.3: Gut analysis of several *Ancistrus* specimens showed a preference for soft diatomaceous algae.

Most species of bristlenose graze happily by both day and night, and will continue to do so in aquaria provided they feel secure. Experiments conducted to explore the differences between the reactions of blind species and sighted bristlenoses found that the sighted ones were highly photophobic and would not even feed in dim light. Although some species are light sensitive, most bristlenoses in tanks are quite happy in ordinary lighting. A propensity for hiding is more attributable to timidity than the light itself. Other studies have observed bristlenoses foraging irrespective of the light conditions.

Keeping Bristlenoses in the aquarium 4

Buying a bristlenose

To the confirmed bristlenose addict seeking a new and unusual species, the following advice will probably be irrelevant. Unusual species are found in the aquatic shop with the same feeling with which a gold miner sees the little speck of yellow in his pan and such buyers will often pay outrageous prices for fish in less than perfect condition. These fish are carried home, with fingers crossed, to be subjected to a regime of dedicated care and attention in the hope that they will recover. This is not, however, a recommended practice and can prove extremely expensive!

Figure 4.1: This male '*hoplogenys*-type' is fit and well but many similar imports can be close to death.

For a newcomer seeking an interesting addition to the community aquarium, the best buy is undoubtedly a group of little tank-bred fish. The advantages of this are manifold. Fish spawned and raised by other hobbyists are likely to be in far better condition. The farthest they have travelled is from one tank to another, probably a short local journey. They have not been subjected to the trauma of being hauled out of their home rivers, packed together in boxes and flown long distances to be kept in totally different water conditions. These little fish are unlikely to carry any strange and exotic diseases or parasites, and to be well adapted to your local water conditions (assuming you are buying them in a local shop). Since the fish will be siblings, they are obviously guaranteed to be of the same species and, when they grow, you are likely to be able to spawn them successfully yourself. They will be priced at a sum that won't break the bank and, by buying and raising a group (to ensure that you get a pair), you may well be able to make a profit by selling the extras later when they are grown. These tank bred fry are nearly always *Ancistrus temmincki* or *cirrhosus*, although at this age neither you nor anyone else stands a chance of being sure of the identification.

Figure 4.2: Small tank-bred fish like these albino *cirrhosus* are often a better buy than large wild-caught specimens.

The temptation is always there to spend the extra money and come home with full-grown fish, sporting huge bristles. Although these are often superb fish, this is not recommended for a beginner. Although your large fish may have been evicted from another aquarist's aquarium as they grew, the small and peaceful bristlenose ends up as a cast-off far less frequently than some of the giant 'plecs'. The odds are that large fish are wild-caught, with all the attendant problems of possible stress and exotic disease. While many such fish do settle down and become active, visible members of the aquarium, many others remain shy and terrified all their lives. You could be paying a lot of money for a fish you will never see. The little fry who are usually out and about in search of food will grow into active, confident adults who are also invariably out and about. If you buy a fish that is constantly trying to hide, it is likely to continue to do so.

If you have decided to buy full-grown (or juvenile wild) fish anyway, because you specifically want that species, there are a few danger signs to look out for.

Bristlenoses vary in colour from pale brown to jet black, with or without a variety of spots and markings. Albino and leucistic forms are orange-pink in colour. Under no circumstances are they naturally adorned with uneven white patches and any fish that is

Figure 4.3: This male is happy to be out and about with the other community residents even when there is no food on offer.

should be avoided. These patches are caused by damage, often from bad handling or aggression between the fish while packed unnaturally close to each other. This is bad enough; occasionally lesions are visible with the white patch spreading out from the damaged area and such fish are unlikely to survive. Tanks with dead fish in them are to be avoided and even seemingly healthy fish from that tank should be left in the shop.

Before buying, try to see the fish up against the glass. If it will not do this naturally, ask the shopkeeper to bring the fish up against the glass while catching it or inspect it in the plastic bag. The stomach should be slightly rounded, and gently pressing against the glass or bag. Since the back and sides of a bristlenose are covered with hard bony scutes, they cannot change shape. A bristlenose in the last stages of starvation is no thinner, looked at from the top, than a glutton. The only area that can show this is the unarmoured stomach; fish with hollow, concave bellies are not feeding. This may be because they are new imports and haven't had time to catch up on their meals. If you suspect this ask the shopkeeper to reserve the fish (you may need to pay a small deposit) and come back in a couple of weeks. By this time the fish will either be fatter, or possibly dead. If you buy a fish that is not eating, it may well never eat and will die. Bristlenoses are not fussy about their food and healthy fish eat non-stop given the opportunity. Fish that will not eat may be suffering from disease or internal damage.

Figure 4.4: The well rounded stomach of this gold marble *Ancistrus* shows it is healthy and eating well.

Finally, when you have chosen your fish, watch while they are caught for you. Bristlenoses are extremely prickly and can become entangled in nets. If the person serving you is inexperienced or impatient, the fish can become severely damaged by wrenching it out carelessly. Bristlenoses like lots of oxygen and should be packed in big bags with oxygen added. Never allow two adult males to be packed together - the close confines of a bag could well lead to open warfare.

If you have bought the fish from your local shop, then it will already be in water similar to your own. If you have bought the fish some distance away, or even in another country, you will need to test the water it is in. If it varies from your own in pH or hardness, you will need to acclimatise the fish slowly. Place the fish in an aquarium (or bucket) of a size so that the water it came in is sufficient to cover the fish and an aquarium heater. Position a bucket of clean, dechlorinated water slightly higher than the tank the fish is in, and set up an air line to siphon the water from the bucket into the fish aquarium. The water should just be dripping through the siphon, rather than flowing. If it is going too fast, use a bulldog clip to restrict the flow through the airline. After about a day the bucket will be empty, the aquarium full, and the fish acclimatised to the water.

Figure 4.5: Acclimatise fish to new water conditions slowly.

Providing a suitable home

Companions in the community aquarium

Bristlenoses are ideal community fish, and will get on well with most other aquarium inhabitants. However, as they like moving waters with lots of oxygen, they cannot be expected to share with fish such as anabantoids, that require very still, calm aquaria.

Being armoured catfish that spend most of their time on the substrate, they are not usually victims of bullying. The exception to this would be fish that are very protective of eggs - a bristlenose grazing across the glass and aquarium furniture can appear as a threat. Nonetheless, some species are shyer than others and may feel overawed if kept with fish which are larger than themselves or excessively boisterous.They are placid fish who are only likely to threaten other aquarium inhabitants if guarding spawn. Even then, damage to other fish is extremely unlikely as they are unwieldy swimmers and could not pursue their tankmates through the water even if they wanted to. They can be trusted with the tiniest fish - even fry are safe once they are free-swimming. Unlike some of the larger plecs, which can occasionally become 'rogue', or the vicious sucking loach, with its unpleasant tendency to rasp flesh off its tank-mates, the bristlenose is a tireless worker in the aquarium and causes no harm to plants or fish.

Figure 4.6: This bristlenose is quite happy for the *corydoras* to feed peacefully beside him.

Equipment and furnishings

Within the aquarium, the fish require good filtration and plenty of water movement. A pair of internal filters, or an internal filter and a powerhead drawing water through an undergravel filter, is ideal. By having two devices the risk of an equipment failure killing the fish before it is noticed is minimised. The more water movement and oxygenation that is going on, the better the fish will like it.

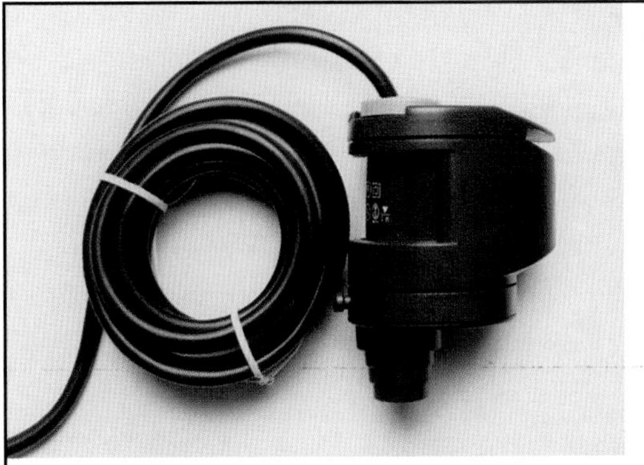

Figure 4.7: A powerhead can be used to drive an undergravel filter and gives far more water movement than an air pump.

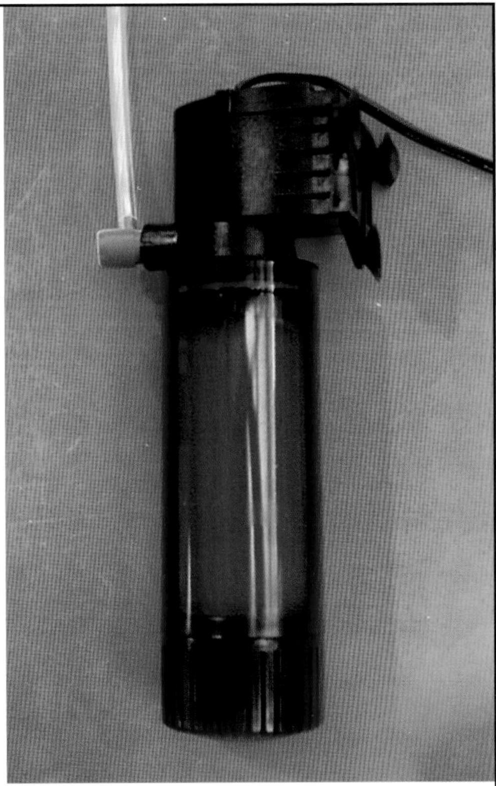

Figure 4.8: An internal power filter is also a good choice, providing lots of water current.

Figure 4.9: Powerheads and filters with venturi devices included add even more aeration, blowing a stream of bubbles out with the water.

The substrate can be either gravel or sand but needs to be kept clean. This is of course true for any fish, but a bottom-dweller such as a bristlenose will feel the ill-effects of a dirty substrate first. The decor should include lots of hiding places. The temptation is to minimise the hiding places so that the fish can be better seen but this will just result in stressed and unhappy fish. With ample nooks and crannies to hide in, the fish will feel safe enough to venture out regularly. The tank should include at least one piece of bogwood because bristlenoses enjoy chewing on this. It is thought that the wood supplies lignin, which may be a vital part of their diet. Since it will be chewed, obviously the wood must be untreated and unvarnished.

Caves and crannies can also be constructed from pipes, stacked slates, and rocks. If rocks and slates are used, ensure that the structure is stable - they can be glued together outside the tank with silicon glue if necessary. Unstable rockwork may collapse, squashing the fish or even breaking the aquarium glass. Bristlenoses seem to prefer long thin crevices into which they only just fit (although make sure that the size is sufficient to avoid the fish getting stuck!)

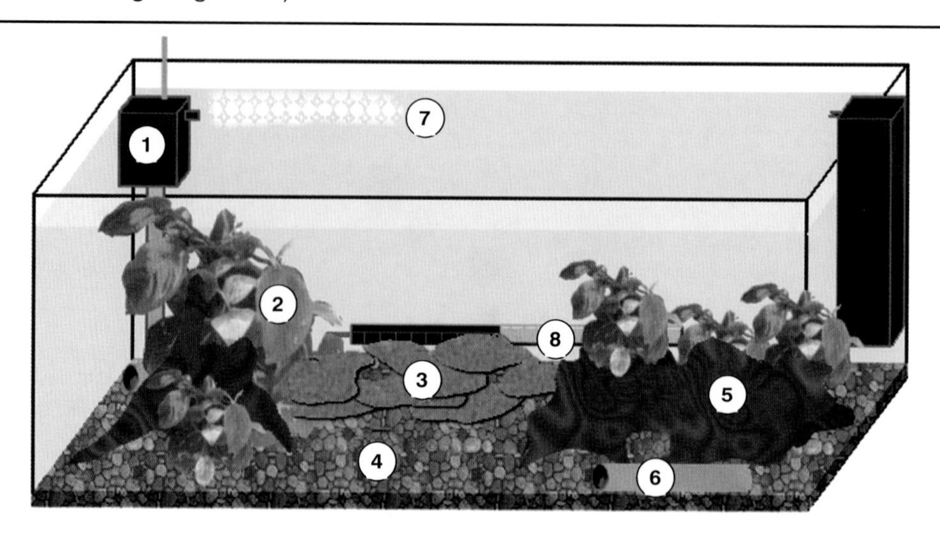

1 • Two filtration devices ensure good water flow and provide a backup for each other.

2 • Bristlenoses will not damage plants, so you can use them in landscaping. Anubias and Java Fern will grow in less light than most plants.

3 • Stack or glue together flat rocks to create caves.

4 • Leave an open area at the front so you can feed the fish where you can see them.

5 • Bogwood creates caves and crannies and is a necessary part of the diet.

6 • Pipes can also be used to create potential spawning sites.

7 • Venturi devices on powerheads and filters give extra oxygenation.

8 • The temperature in an ordinary tropical community will suit most species but some may prefer it warmer.

Figure 4.12: An aquarium suitably equipped for bristlenoses.

Lighting

These fish are most active at dawn and dusk in nature, although still foraging both during the day and night. In the aquarium your fish will be shyer and more retiring if they are subjected to bright lighting. The single tube that fits into most standard aquarium hoods is perfectly adequate for bristlenoses, although not enough for serious plant growing. If you want a planted aquarium containing bristlenoses, choose plants that can survive in low light such as Java Fern, *Anubias,* and *Cryptocorynes*. All these do well in a bristlenose tank. In spite of their vegetarian diet, bristlenoses will do no harm to aquarium plants and will carefully graze the algae off the leaves without harming the plant. *Anubias* and Java Fern can be grown attached to bogwood instead of in the substrate. A rubber band can be used to keep them in place while their roots take hold. Black cotton, as is often recommended, can snare and kill bristlenoses.

Tank size and stocking

When adult, the fish will be approximately four inches long and thus require an allocation of forty-eight square inches of surface area each. This does not mean that you can pack six bristlenoses into a two-foot tank. They require a reasonable amount of space; a three-foot tank would accommodate a trio (one male and two females) or a pair. This is the minimum size aquarium that should be considered. The remaining space in the aquarium can be used by an assortment of community fish.

Unless there is only one male, the question of territory then needs to be considered. Male bristlenoses are usually described as aggressive to one another. Experiments to prove this usually start “one male with eggs was placed in close proximity to another male with eggs”. In these circumstances vicious fights will, unsurprisingly, result, while in less unnatural and forced conditions they are a great deal more peaceful. In a four foot aquarium I have three pairs of bristlenoses - all three males have chosen to establish ‘territories’ within the same end of the tank (oddly enough, the end where the food goes in). A ‘territory’ for a bristlenose simply constitutes his own crevice. There need to be enough hiding places for the fish to be able to choose one of his own accord so that he can select a residence near another or at the opposite end of the tank, as he wishes. There needs to be ample room for the fish to get away from each other when they want to - this is the subtle difference between choosing to have a flatmate and being locked up in a cell with someone.

The interplay between the three males in the four foot tank is fascinating to watch. A male requiring privacy will, on seeing another making his way over the gravel, casually

Figure 4.13: This male has chosen an unusually exposed site as 'home' and keeps an eye out for intruders approaching.

Figure 4.14: Somewhat warily, the same male receives a visitor. No trouble ensues and the second male departs peacefully after a few seconds.

Figure 4.15: Eating is far more interesting than arguing. All three males are now voluntarily within six inches of each other.

raise his interopercular spines without even seeming to look at the intruder. The approaching fish, with equal nonchalance, simply changes course so that he is going in another direction. On other occasions, presumably on the whim of the inhabitant, other males will be allowed to 'visit'.

The females have no defined territory, simply moving from one shelter to another, and are treated in the same way by the males - sometimes with raised spines and sometimes ignored. The fish spawn successfully in this tank without any increased aggression. On one occasion I found a batch of eggs being guarded by what appeared to be two proud fathers, with two males side by side occupied in the business of fanning water. They maintained their co-parenting for three days until the spawn was removed to a rearing tank.

Water parameters

South American Amazon waters are usually very soft and vary between slightly and extremely acidic, but bristlenoses are more tolerant than many other South American fish. For general keeping, all the species can be acclimatised to either hard and/or alkaline waters. Water anywhere between 5.5 pH to 7.8 pH and between 2 and 30 dGH will be suitable. The common bristlenoses, *temmincki* and *cirrhosus*, will also spawn happily and prolifically in these conditions. Other species, of which *hoplogenys* appears to be one, may require soft water to spawn; current reports of *hoplogenys* spawnings suggest aiming for under 15dGH, and water between 5.5 and 7pH.

Temperature

Bristlenoses extend through most of North and Central South America and the temperatures in their different home waters vary considerably. Some species are found in temperatures as high as 90°F. A temperature of around 78°F is suitable for them all, however, as well as being appreciated by the other community residents. If the temperature is increased (either deliberately or by a warmer room temperature) the bristlenoses will be quite happy provided oxygen levels are kept up.

Feeding your fish

The Loricariidae family is often referred to as 'algae-eaters'. While this is more true of some species than others, bristlenoses in the wild do indeed subsist mainly on algae. In the aquarium they will clean up murky green walls with a speed that is nothing short of miraculous. This ability means that within a very short space of time, the aquarium bristlenoses find themselves short of food - algae cannot possibly grow fast enough, even in a large tank, to support a hungry bristlenose. They cannot, therefore, just be left to their own devices but, like all aquarium fish, need to be provided with a suitable diet by their owner.

In keeping with their natural diet, bristlenoses have very long intestinal tracts to assist in extracting nutrition from vegetable foods. Their diet in the aquarium should also be predominantly vegetarian - a completely carnivorous diet would result in the intestine starting to malfunction.

There are a wide variety of vegetables suitable for feeding, which should be blanched (dipped in boiling water) before being used. This breaks down the cellulose, making the food easier to digest. This is necessary because aquatic plants and algae do not have the same cellulose structure as terrestrial plants, which is why they collapse when taken out of water. Cucumber, courgette, lettuce, spinach, squash, boiled potato, and shelled peas are just a few vegetables which will be enjoyed. Fish do have individual preferences and you may find that some fish will enjoy a type of vegetable which others will not touch.

In most of my tanks, when offered a piece of cucumber, the bristlenoses will carefully hollow out the soft interior, leaving the tough skin until there is nothing else left. In another tank, however, the tough skin is carefully peeled off first as a delicacy and the soft flesh left uneaten. In addition to fresh vegetables, you can also feed sinking vegetable-based pellets, algae wafers, and vegetable-based flake food (hold it underwater for a few seconds to ensure it sinks, otherwise the other community fish will eat it before the bristlenoses get a chance).

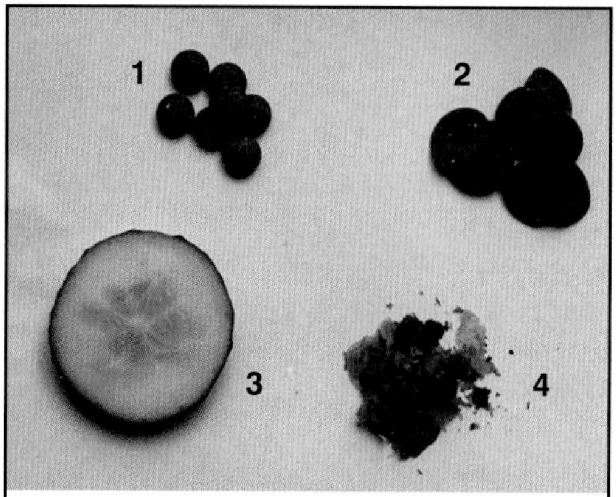

Figure 4.17: Staple food for Bristlenoses.
1. Sinking algae pellets
2. Algae wafers
3. Fresh vegetables
4. Vegetable-based flake food

Figure 4.18: Occasional food items.
1. High protein sinking catfish pellet
2. Frozen (or live) bloodworm
3. Frozen daphnia
4. Frozen glassworm

Algae wafers and flake food are important for species such as *ranunculus*, who do not appear to recognise vegetables as food. These fish prefer a higher meat constituent in their diet, which can be bulked up with dried foods.

As mentioned previously, the fish also need to be able to chew at a piece of bogwood. Although predominantly vegetarian, wild bristlenoses also enjoy insect larvae, and high protein foods should form an occasional part of the diet. For a weekly treat you can feed live or frozen bloodworm, frozen daphnia or mosquito larvae, peeled prawns, or high protein sinking pellets. These foods may also be useful if you are trying to spawn the fish, to encourage a new arrival to eat, or to condition a badly stressed or damaged purchase. In these circumstances, the meat foods may be fed more often but should not be allowed to form the major part of the diet on a permanent basis.

You will also find that your bristlenoses will eat the corpses of any fish that die in the aquarium. Although this should not be encouraged, as it can spread disease, you will often find that they have been too quick for you and that a fish appears to have simply vanished. This is not anything to worry about and you can feel sure that the fish had died before they ate it. Bristlenoses do not attack even sick fish and can be trusted with any equally peaceful fish of any size.

The overriding interest which most bristlenoses have for food can be a great asset to the aquarist. By always feeding at the front of the aquarium and staying beside the aquarium at least for a while when the food goes in, the bristlenoses will learn that not only do you mean them no harm but that your presence heralds the arrival of food. It is sometimes recommended that they should be fed just before the lights are switched off, on the basis that they are too shy to feed otherwise. There is absolutely no need for this, unless you want to actively encourage shy fish. The benefits of ensuring your bristlenoses are familiar with you exceed the simple pleasure of seeing them more often. If the fish need to be caught, for treatment or to be moved, tame fish can often be caught in the hand with a minimum of fuss, avoiding the possibilities of damage if nets are used and the stress of being pursued around the tank for hours. Spawning males are less likely to panic and knock their egg clump off when you are near or when you need to move the spawn and much more of the day to day life of your fish will be visible to you.

Diseases and disorders

Bristlenoses are tough and hardy fish, and diseases and disorders are fortunately rare. For the most part, problems will occur with new, wild-caught specimens which should ideally be quarantined carefully for a period of several months before being let near your established stock. One of their more novel forms of behaviour, which can cause alarm, is a habit of taking a rest lying upside down. This is more likely to be noticeable in aquaria where the fish are relaxed and tame, as in this position the bristlenose has its soft underbelly exposed and is very vulnerable. Nonetheless, they seem to like to rest in this position and will then turn the right way up after a while to move around the aquarium. They are

Figure 4.19: This male is not sick, just taking a rest after a hard day's work eating the cucumber that was originally enclosed in the lead strip.

certainly not dead, or even sick. After a while you will stop having panic attacks when you see them doing this.

Bacterial infections

Hollow-bellied fish that will not eat probably have a disease, rather than simply disliking all the food you are offering them. Although you should offer them a good variety of food, and try live blood-worm to tempt them, the real problem is likely to be something else. Bacterial infections are common. If you are able to get antibiotics (you may need to see a vet in some countries) then this would be a good start. However, many imports which were coping with their infections reasonably well in the wild state, have now been stressed and traumatised by their travels and the bacteria will have gained a far more drastic hold. Such fish are likely to die anyway, as by the time you get them the damage is too great. You can do your best, but I do not recommend that you buy fish in this state.

Worm infestations

Another cause of hollow bellies and a wasted appearance is an infestation of parasites such as tapeworms and roundworms. Perversely, these can also cause an obesely fat appearance, where the worms are so large or numerous that they are distending the body. Treatments are available for these parasites but are best obtained in consultation with a vet. Unfortunately, an advanced infestation is likely to have damaged the fish beyond the likelihood of a cure. In either of the above circumstances, the fish should be in a quarantine tank anyway, and nowhere near healthy fish. If such a disease becomes apparent after the fish has been added to a community, it should be removed to another tank immediately. On no account should the body be left to be eaten by other fish.

White spot

White spot manifests itself as tiny white cysts all over the fish, including the fins. This is an opportunistic disease which attacks weakened and stressed fish. Sometimes imports will be infected as a result of the stress of travel but other, underlying problems should also be suspected. Bristlenoses are reasonably resistant to the disease,and will usually be the last fish in the tank to be affected by an outbreak. If previously healthy bristlenoses settled in to your aquarium suddenly contract whitespot, you should take a serious look at your aquarium management practices and test the water immediately for toxins such as ammonia and nitrites. Whitespot can be treated by several proprietary medicines available from your local retailer. Bristlenoses are not unduly sensitive to medication but they are sensitive to a reduction in oxygen. Many treatments reduce the dissolved oxygen in the water so an increase in aeration would be a good idea while treatment continues.

Oxygen shortage

Bristlenoses prefer a high level of oxygen in the water and will be one of the first fish to show stress if the level drops. If you see your fish hanging round the top of the tank, looking as though they are trying to climb out, check the pumps immediately. It is always handy to have a spare in case of malfunction and this is a good reason to split the filtration of the tank between two devices. Once the fish are showing this behaviour, instant remedial action must be taken. The next morning will probably be too late. This can be a particular problem in fry tanks. Initially, a huge tank is filled with tiny newly hatched bristlenoses, which can be half an inch long in a couple of weeks. If the aquarist is not prepared for their growth rate, the tank can go from 'plenty of room' to 'dramatically and fatally overstocked' almost overnight. If the little fry are all ringing the top of the tank at the water surface, they will all be dead in a couple of hours without extra aeration immediately.

Figure 4.21: This *ranunculus* is not sick. The white patches form part of an even pattern shared by his tankmates. This fish has been in residence for a year, is eating well and behaving normally. Similar patches, especially those uneven in size and location, can be a sign of damage and need to be watched carefully.

Fungus

Fungal infections are also opportunistic, striking when the fish has already been damaged. The fluffy white tufts usually grow at the site of a skin break, caused either by bad handling and transit or by scraping in crevices with sharp corners in the aquarium. Fungal infections respond well to a broad spectrum bactericide/fungicide such as Myxazin. The pale white patches on fish that have recently been imported do not appear to be fungal and rarely require special treatment. High standards of water quality, strong oxygenation, a peaceful aquarium and good feeding are the best remedy for these.

5 Spawning the Bristlenose

Spawning triggers

Methods of persuading recalcitrant bristlenoses to spawn are poorly understood. Certainly they are quite capable of spawning all year round, with no noticeable special treatment whatsoever. Most bristlenose spawnings 'just happen' - often the first the aquarist knows about it is when the tiny fry are seen out and about in the tank. Provided you have an adult male and female (the males have larger and more numerous bristles than the females, in most species the females have none) there is no reason such a pleasant surprise should not happen to you.

If you want to spawn some of the more unusual species, it may be necessary to provide softer, more acidic water, mimicking their natural rivers and streams. While remarkably adaptable in ordinary living conditions, some species may not spawn in hard waters and, if they do, the eggs may die. Try to reduce the pH and hardness as much as you can. In some South American waters the pH is below 4 and hardness is negligible. These changes need to be made slowly - if you suddenly place the fish into water of a vastly different composition to the water they are used to, they will be badly traumatised and may die. Either way, they certainly won't spawn.

In their natural environment bristlenoses, like most other South American fish, are often forced into seasonal spawning by necessity. In the dry season adult fish need all their energy for survival, either losing weight or managing to sustain their weight without growth. When the rains come, a number of factors make it a good time for the fish to spawn. Depending on the area they come from, their natural home may experience long periods of high water or only a relatively short season.

The rains, both directly in the area and floodwaters sweeping down from higher altitudes, cause a rise in the water level, up to twelve metres in some places. As the water rises, previously terrestrial areas are now submerged. A whole new landscape packed with suitable spawning sites is now available. Those parts of the river which were the shallow algae beds are now deeper. Adult fish that were vulnerable in the shallow waters can now graze there with greater security. With the flooding covering areas of previously terrestrial vegetation, plant matter (and probably a good amount of animal matter too) decomposes. The nutrient levels of the water rise, promoting vigorous algae growth and providing even more food.

In the aquarium, we can ensure that our fish have an ample number of spawning sites to choose from and are well-fed all year round. In addition to the increased food and territory supplies, the rainy season also brings faster currents and increased oxygenation as the flood waters pour towards the sea. Once again, good water movement and aeration can be given to our fish throughout the year, although a little extra can always be added.

	9/12/67 (pre-rainy season)	23/12/67 (after the event of the rains)
pH	5.1	5.2
Conductivity at 28°C (µS)	13	18
Total Hardness (°dH)	0.075	0.195
$KMn0_4$ Oxidation (mg/l)	23	33
Total Nitrogen (µg/l)	110	240
Total Phosphorus (µg/l)	2.8	4.5
Total Iron (µg/l)	198	211

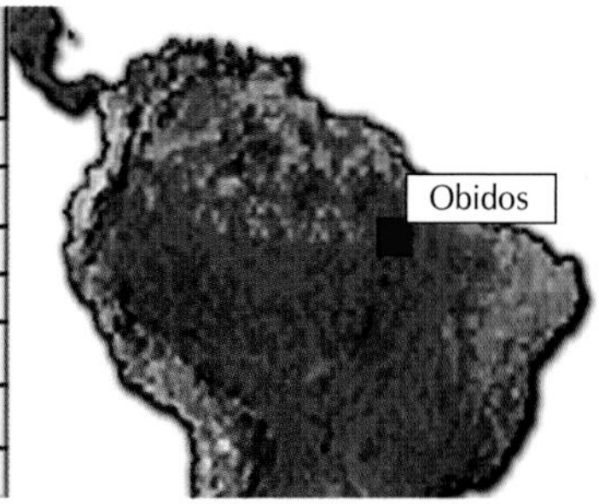

Obidos

Table 5.1: Water chemistry changes before and after the start of the rainy season in the Rio Curucamba at Obidos. Taken from R Geisler, H A Knoppel and H Sioloi's Ecology of the Freshwater Fishes of Amazonia 1971.

Table 5.1 shows changes measured in water chemistry before and after the onset of the rainy season at Obidos.

In spite of having an ideal set-up all year round, some pairs are still determinedly seasonal, spawning in the winter months regardless of the efforts of the aquarist or known changes in the aquarium conditions. Since such behaviour cannot be attributed to the water chemistry, hours of daylight, or conditions in the tank, which are all controlled directly by the aquarist, another factor outside the aquarist's control must be suspected.

Air pressure was suggested as a spawning factor in 1952 for various South American fish. In an article in the *Aquarist*, Christopher Frame observed that his fishes spawned successfully when the barometer was rising, but not when falling. The fish he listed as being stimulated to spawn included *Hemigrammus ocellifer*, the beacon or head and tail light, *Pristella maxillaris*, the X-ray fish, and other *Hemigrammus* species. Dr David Sands, in his 1994 thesis Behavioural and Evolutionary Ecology of *Corydoras adolfoi* and *Corydoras imitator*, observed that a captive group of *Corydoras imitator* spawned after a rise in pressure followed by a sharp fall.

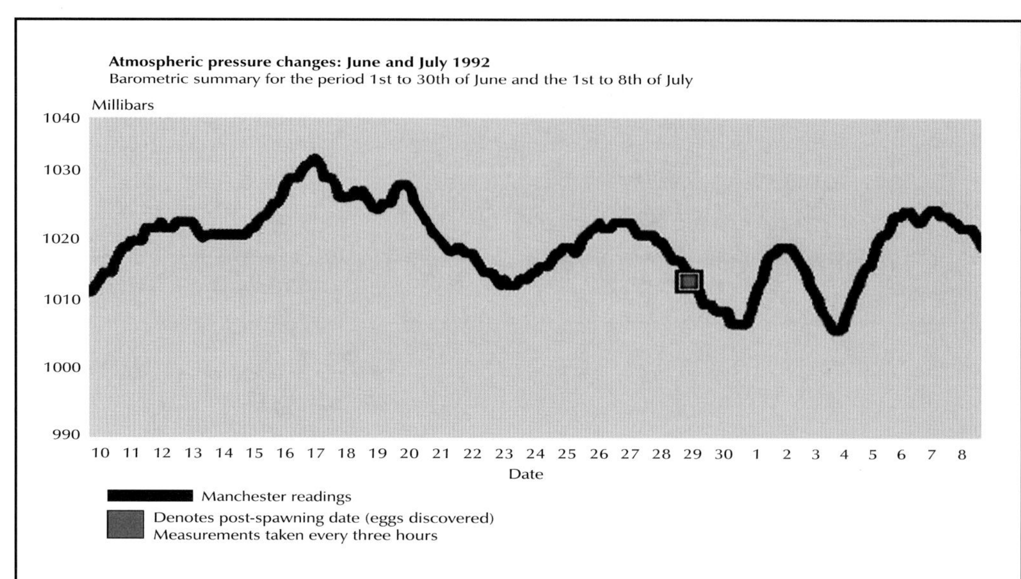

Table 5.2: Spawnings of *Corydoras imitator* were possibly influenced by barometric changes (Dr D Sands 1994).

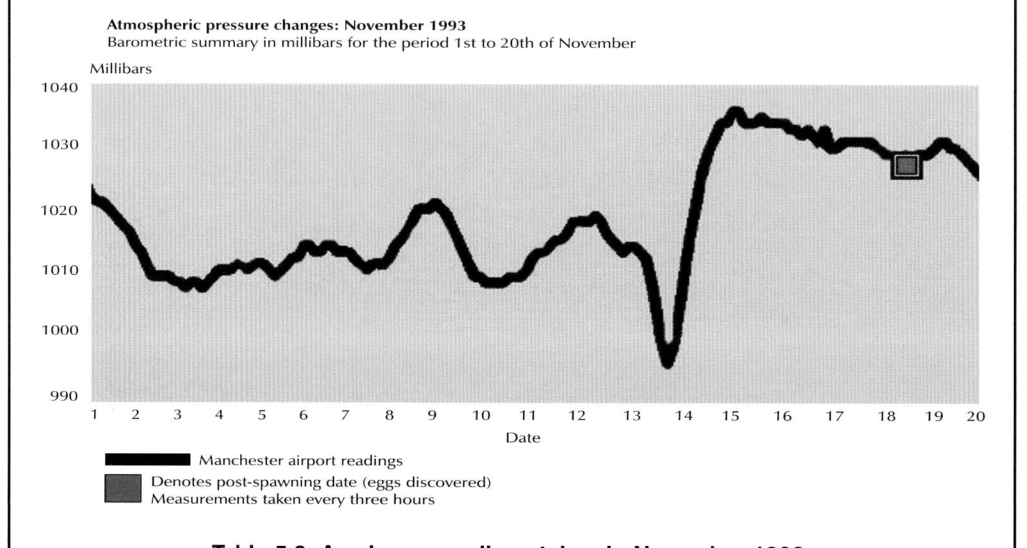

Table 5.3: As above, readings taken in November 1993.

It is noticeable that captive bristlenoses tend to regard the winter months (October - December) as being the spawning season, regardless of their home waters. Since the rainy season occurs at different times in different places in South America, this is unlikely to be controlled by a simple 'biological clock'.

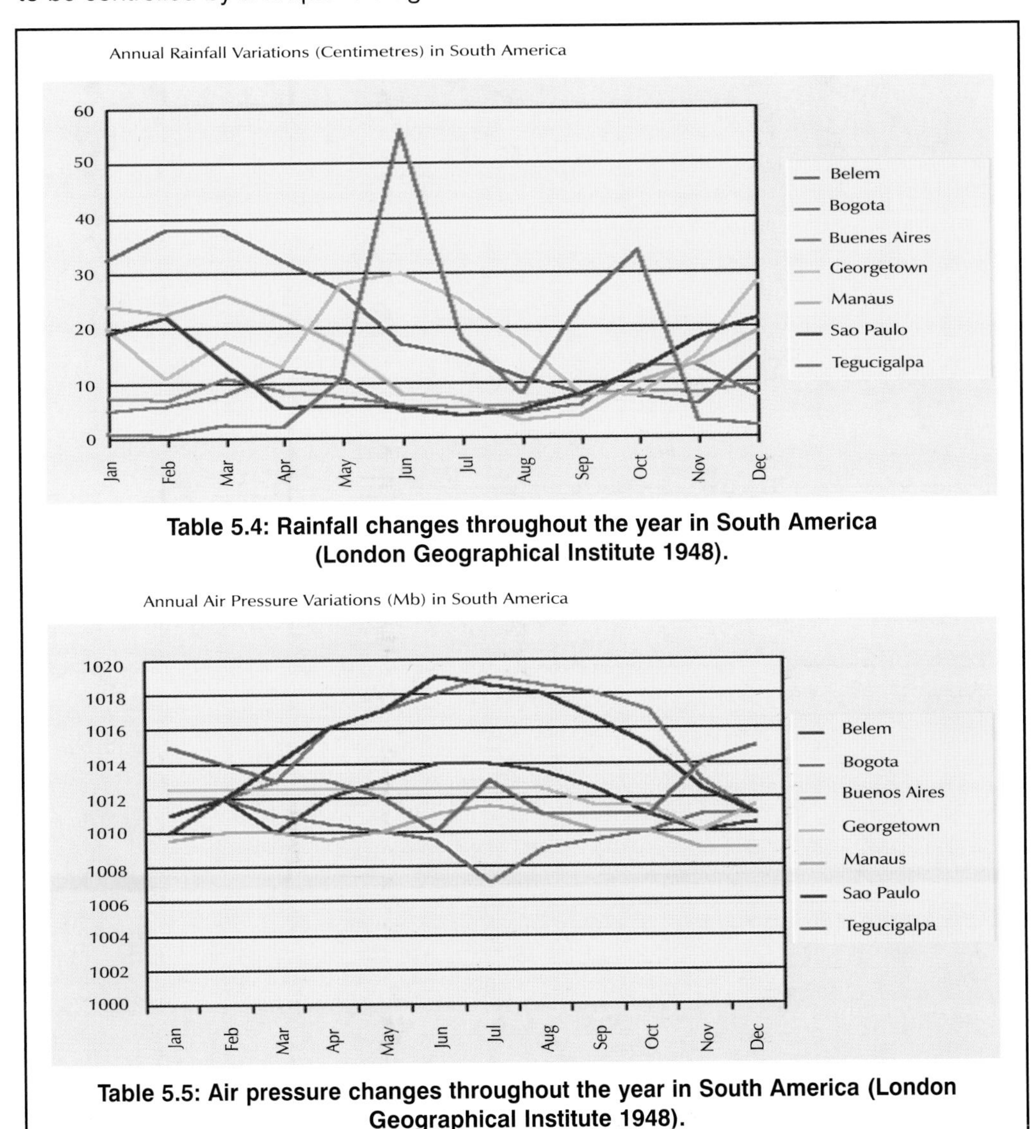

Table 5.4: Rainfall changes throughout the year in South America (London Geographical Institute 1948).

Table 5.5: Air pressure changes throughout the year in South America (London Geographical Institute 1948).

Tables 5.4 and 5.5 show the rainfall and air pressure throughout the year in a variety of South American locations. It can be seen that the rainy season is characterised with lower air pressures, with the pressure rising as the rains reduce.

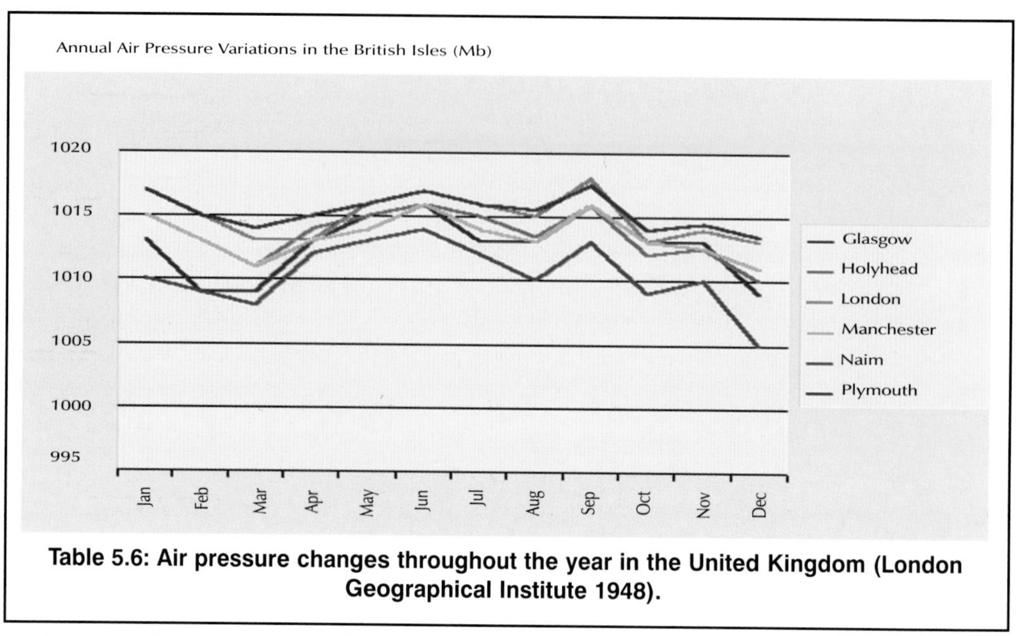

Table 5.6: Air pressure changes throughout the year in the United Kingdom (London Geographical Institute 1948).

In table 5.6 it can be seen that in the United Kingdom air pressure rises just before the winter, then falls steadily towards December - the very period when seasonally inclined bristlenoses choose to spawn. The tables show average data over a period of thirty-five years.

This information is of absolutely no practical use as aquarists cannot exert control over the air pressure. It may provide some explanation, however, as to why the fish spawn suddenly after months of ignoring every effort to induce them to produce offspring. On occasion young fish may start to spawn in the winter period but settle down into all-year production as they become more mature. Seasonal spawning is more likely to be a factor for wild-caught specimens than for tank-bred individuals.

Pre-spawning and spawning behaviour

Once the male has found a suitable crevice and taken up residence, a female near to the point of spawning approaches for an examination of both the potential husband and the prospective spawning site. At this time the aquarist may be alerted to the fact that something is going on by the skittishness of both fish. At first the male may chase the female away, starting with full-scale chases across the tank. She appears to know that no real harm is intended because very soon she is back, poking her nose into the crevice. The chasing may continue for some days, with varying degrees of vigour. On one occasion I observed a pair of *temminck*i pursuing one another round and round the bogwood which contained the eventual nesting site. They kept up this circular chase for over quarter of an hour. Some observers have claimed that the male may slap the surface of the water with his tail to draw the female's attention, or pursue her to attract her attention. In all the pairs that I know, the male is fairly indifferent until the female has made an approach and certainly makes no visible attempt to lure the female. However, behaviour varies considerably between individual fish, and even between different spawnings of the same fish. The chasing can be prolonged or non-existent.

When the chasing stops, the female enters the crevice where she lays the eggs. Since the male is now effectively evicted, there is only room for his back end which one must assume is doing its work near the eggs. This is convenient because it leaves his front, prickly, end free to threaten anything that approaches at this vulnerable time. A spawning can often be spotted by the sight of a male bristlenose half out of his hole in a full threat display for no apparent reason.

Figure 5.2 shows a male *Ancistrus temmincki* in this position, with the female inside the crevice. At this point the female has been inside for about four minutes.

Figure 5.2: Male *Ancistrus temmincki* in threat position during spawning. Note the everted interopercular spines to deter visitors.

Figure 5.3: The newly laid eggs are briefly exposed to the camera.

The newly laid eggs are yellow to bright orange in colour (depending on species) and form a clump like a giant orange raspberry. These can range from twenty or so eggs from an adolescent pair up to two hundred in a fully mature female. The spawning pictured resulted in one-hundred and twenty-three fry with no known mortality. In the mating of the tame and friendly pair being photographed, the male moved out of the way to let the female leave the spawning site, affording a clear view of the eggs. In many spawnings the eggs will be completely invisible, constantly shielded by the male, and the aquarist will only be able to deduce their presence by the male's behaviour.

As soon as the eggs are laid, or very shortly afterwards, the male takes up his station in the crevice, guarding the spawn. Except in unusual circumstances, he will remain there for up to two weeks, protecting first the eggs and then the new fry. During this time he does not eat and will only come out if completely panic-stricken. I once tried to dislodge the male in the photographs to take further pictures of the developing spawn. He simply hung on tight, locked his fins in the upright position and was unshakeable. Attempts to move him resulted in an extremely large piece of bogwood coming away as well, so the attempt was abandoned for fear of damaging him.

Figure 5.4: The male takes up his guarding position which he will maintain until all the fry have left home.

Figure 5.5: The male is often attached to the eggs by his sensitive mouth, cleaning and protecting them.

Within the crevice the male is often attached to the egg clump by his mouth, continually cleaning the spawn. The pectoral fins make circular movements, wafting clean oxygenated water over the eggs. The care provided by the male is nearly impossible to duplicate and attempts to hatch the eggs artificially are usually thwarted by the spread of fungus as the embryos die. Occasionally a spawn is positioned on the roof of the crevice and the male's weight can dislodge the clump. Eggs that are dislodged in this way are likely to die, in spite of the male following them and attaching himself to them wherever they have rolled. It is likely that the confines of the crevice lend themselves to an easily maintained directional water flow and that, in open ground, the male is unable to create adequate currents. The urge of a male bristlenose to guard eggs is so strong that males have been documented 'adopting' a spawn that was not theirs. In the episode described earlier, where two males appeared to be 'co-parenting' a batch of eggs, both were occupied with the characteristic movements of the pectoral fins, guiding the water over the oxygen-hungry eggs.

Once the female has laid the eggs, she usually takes no further interest in them. She will not harm the spawn or the new fry and can safely be left in the tank. In this particular pair, the female took an unusual interest, visiting the spawn two days later. The male was unperturbed by this and moved out of the way so that she could perform her inspection. More such visits may have gone unrecorded. It was fortuitous that I happened to have a camera ready when this one took place.

Figure 5.6: This female took more of an interest than is usual.

Raising the fry

After four or five days, the eggs hatch. The precise moment of hatching can be difficult to determine because the male is still firmly attached to the spawn. Even if you can see the eggs, newly hatched bristlenoses look very like bristlenose eggs - they are almost entirely composed of a huge yolk with a tiny splinter of tail attached.

Figure 5.7: This newly hatched fry is sitting on a ten pence (25 cent) coin.

Very shortly after hatching, the fry will start to escape parental care. Increasing numbers of tiny yellow balloons will be seen clustering in corners of the tank. Ideally, the spawning pair will be residing in their own aquarium, having been relocated in anticipation of the happy event. Bristlenoses seem to enjoy thwarting these endeavours and often refuse to spawn in their new home only to instantly produce a family on their return to the community aquarium. If this occurs it is sensible to move the male, complete with his eggs and the piece of decor containing his crevice, to another tank before the fry start escaping parental control. These escapees are very vulnerable to attack by other residents of a community aquarium and can also be sucked into internal filters. Males who are familiar with their owners take being moved in their stride. The simplest method is to place a very large plastic bag in the tank and manoeuvre the decor with attached fish and eggs into the bag. The whole lot can then be moved to the new tank without ever being out of water. Any stray fry can be easily and safely rounded up with a transparent turkey baster which is far easier to manipulate than the traditional method of siphoning them out through a piece of airline.

The water in the new tank should be at the same temperature and water chemistry as the aquarium from which the fish have come, and plenty of filtration and aeration must be provided. Internal power filters are not suitable for a fry tank as the little fish will get

Figure 5.8: A transparent turkey baster is ideal for rounding up tiny fry.

Figure 5.9: These air-powered corner filters are placed on the substrate.

Figure 5.10: This air-powered sponge filter sits on the substrate.

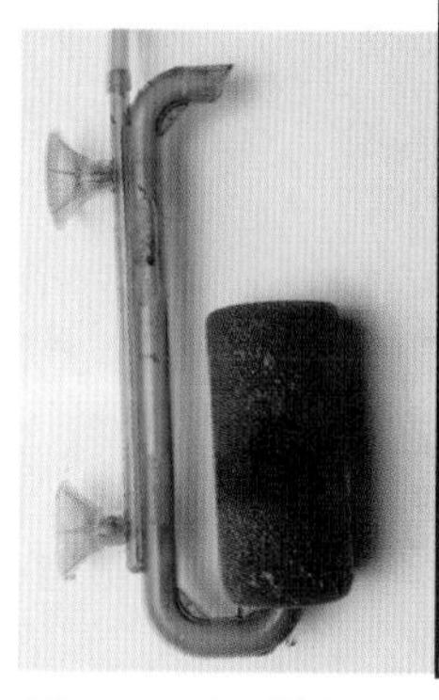

Figure 5.11: This sponge filter fits onto the side of the tank.

Figures 5.9-5.11: A variety of air-powered filters are safe for fry. Growing fry can also graze on micro-organisms growing on sponge filters.

sucked into the filter and die. An undergravel filter with a powerhead will supply good filtration as well as the essential water currents. Many powerheads also incorporate a venturi, which will help with oxygenating the water. Internal sponge filters are also suitable.

There cannot be too much air going through the water and it is better to err on the side of excess. A few airlines attached to an air pump can be included in addition to the filtration system. Whichever filtration method is chosen, it should incorporate at least two devices (two sponge filters with an airpump each or a sponge filter and an undergravel filter). This ensures that if one should fail, the growing fry will be supported until it is replaced. Ideally the tank should have a flourishing algae growth to feed the new fry. A tank can be prepared a few weeks earlier and left in direct sunlight; by the time the bristlenose family are ready to move in it should be thick with algae. Since a single spawning can have more than a hundred fry, as large a tank as possible should be set aside for them. If you only have a small tank, this is better than leaving them in the community aquarium but be aware that the numbers will need to be thinned on a regular basis.

A two foot tank is adequate for raising about twenty fry to a size where they can be distributed in community aquaria without being eaten.

Figure 5.12: A powerful air pump can drive an air-powered filter and an extra airline and airstone, providing even more oxygenation and water movement.

Ideally the eggs should be moved on around the third day and, on no account, should they be moved without their father. Without parental care the spawn will almost certainly die. In ideal circumstances the parents would have spawned in an aquarium specially set up for the purposes, but they have their own opinions about suitable accommodation and even long-established pairs sometimes stop spawning completely if they are moved. When the little fry are first seen out and about in the tank it is likely that what appears to be vast quantities of fry collecting in tank corners are only a part of the spawn. Most will still be in the guardianship of the male. However, an early start in life does not appear to put them at any disadvantage in the safety of a rearing tank and the early appearances will grow as well as those who stay with the male. While the yolk sacs are visible the fry are being nourished completely by the yolk and will not take any other food. It is important not to feed them at this stage as any food will only rot and pollute the water.

Figure 5.13: The gangs of fry collecting in corners of the tank are only likely to be a small fraction of the total spawning.

Figure 5.14: The details of the tiny fish can only be seen by magnifying them.

Figure 5.15: At four days old, although still tiny and with remnants of the yolk sac left, the fry are starting to assume adult colouring.

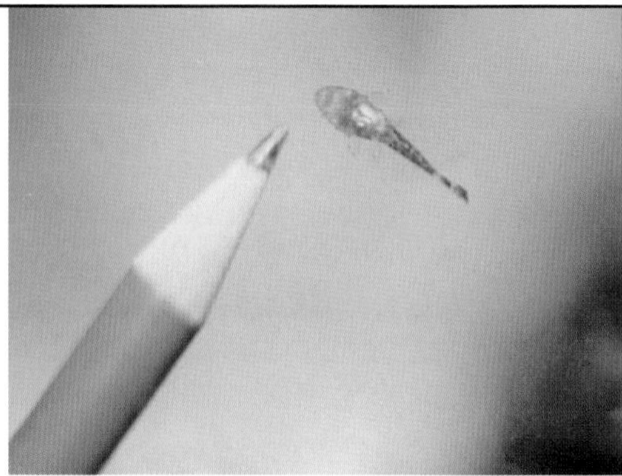

Figure 5.16: At seven days old the fry are perfect, although miniature, copies of their parents.

Once the yolk sacs have completely vanished, at around a week old, the fry are ravenous feeders. To grow well, they need to feed non-stop. Each day they should be given ample vegetable matter to last them until the next day. Anything left of the old feed should be removed when the new feed is given. One hundred growing bristlenoses can eat a remarkable amount and enough should be given so that they don't run out. All the foods the adults enjoy are quite suitable for the little fish who will chew pieces off as required.

The fry grow at a phenomenal rate during this time and a careful eye must be kept open to watch for overstocking problems. If oxygen in the tank runs short, they will be seen edging towards the surface. If a higher proportion than normal are to be found near the top of the tank remedial action needs to be taken. If this is ignored, eventually a day will come when they are all gasping at the waterline; at this stage they are only hours from death. This desperate behaviour should not be confused with the fact that they enjoy water flows. Airstones in the tank will rapidly accumulate a group of bristlenoses sitting in the bubbles and enjoying the current. This is nothing to worry about and, provided some of their siblings are still foraging for food, normally all is well.

Water changes of ten percent daily will keep the water fresh; since they spend ninety per cent of their time eating, it therefore follows that they spend ninety per cent of their time excreting. This is a lot for filters to cope with.

After about a week all the fry will be active in the tank and the male can be returned to his usual home.

After about a month (sooner if you are using a small tank) it will be necessary to thin out the fry. Fortunately there is a never ending demand for even tiny fry and you should have no trouble selling them to local aquatic shops. Don't believe anyone who grudgingly offers to 'take them off your hands' - there is a ready market for them and you should receive at least a small payment or credit note. This process of reducing the numbers of fry needs to be repeated every couple of weeks. It is not unusual for the entire spawn to survive and casualties should be few and far between.

After about two months the remaining fry will be about an inch and a quarter long, a suitable size to take their place in your community aquaria of small fish. Within about six weeks of spawning the adults will be ready to spawn again, so it is not difficult to establish an enjoyable and profitable cottage industry producing bristlenoses!

Figure 5.17: In a couple of months the fry are large enough to be sold or moved into community tanks.

6 Species of Bristlenose

Problems and issues of identification

In 1980 Isbrucker catalogued 51 species of *Ancistrus*, since which time a few more can be 'officially' added to the roll call. This does not take into account all those fish which have passed through with only an 'L' number designation to mark their passage. It seems likely that the eventual number of species will be far higher.

Figure 6.1: ***Xenocara (Ancistrus) hoplogenys*** **syntype from BM (NH): 1849. 11.8.89-91.**

Figure 6.2: ***Xenocara (Ancistrus) latifrons*** **BM (NH): 1869. 5.21.9.**

When the first species of *Ancistrus* were being described, the descriptions relied on text and occasional hand-drawn pictures. Sometimes the specimen would be collected by someone else and the scientist describing it would only see the preserved fish at a later date. Identification based on colour pattern for these early specimens is largely guesswork. Preserved *Ancistrus* are almost universally an unpleasant orange-brown colour with little trace of the original colouring.

Within the text, some descriptions are more precise than others, or oddities arise. What can immediately be seen from the preserved specimens is that they are a different shape; the specifics of shape and form are recorded in the scientific descriptions. Recent describers have had the advantage of extremely precise measuring tools and so have been able to produce very comprehensive sets of measurements. Older descriptions are not as precise, with ratios such as 'half the head length'. Nonetheless, such measurements still serve to demonstrate the different proportions of the fish.

	% of total length				% of head length			counts		
	Head length	Head depth	Head width	Dorsal spine width	Eye diameter	Interorbital width	Snout length	Dorsal fin rays	Anal fin rays	Inter opercular spines
A. cirrhosus	38.4	17	34.1	27.1	13.6	43.4	57.1	I/7	I/4	9-13
A. chagresi	35.7	19.2	30.7	25.2	12.8	47	58.8	I/7	I/3-4	10
A. latifrons	36.3	19.8	30.2	29	15.4	46.2	57.1	I/8	I/4	13-15
A. dolichopterus	38.4	19.2	32	28.8	14.2	45.4	57.1	I/8-9	I/4	6-9
A. temmincki	37.3	18.7	30.4	25.2	13.8	50	55.8	I/7	I/4	10-12
A. hoplogenys	36.9	18.5	32.4	28.7	17.7	47	52.3	I/7	I/4	7-10
A. occidentalis	38.1	19	32.5	31.8	15.3	43.4	57.14	I/7	I/4	9-12
A. brevipinnis	32	16	27.5	19.2	13.3	38.4	50	I/7	I/4	12-14
A. montanus	40	17.7	28.5	24	10	33	62.5	I/7	I/4	14
A. bufonius	33	16.5	33	27	12.5	42.1	53.5	I/7	I/4	12-16
A. stigmaticus	38	19	32.7	25.6	10.8	38.1	55.5	I/7	I/3-4	20-30
A. ranunculus	33	12.1	34.1	16.7	12.7	48.3	59.9	I/7	I/4	7-16

Table 6.1 Proportions of various *Ancistrus* species.

Table 6.1 shows some measurements for different *Ancistrus* species, calculated from Regan (1904) and the modern description of *Ancistrus ranunculus*, while figures 6.3 and 6.4 compare some of the proportions graphically.

From these characteristics, specimens can be identified more confidently even though the colour pattern cannot be judged. By using ratios of different measurements

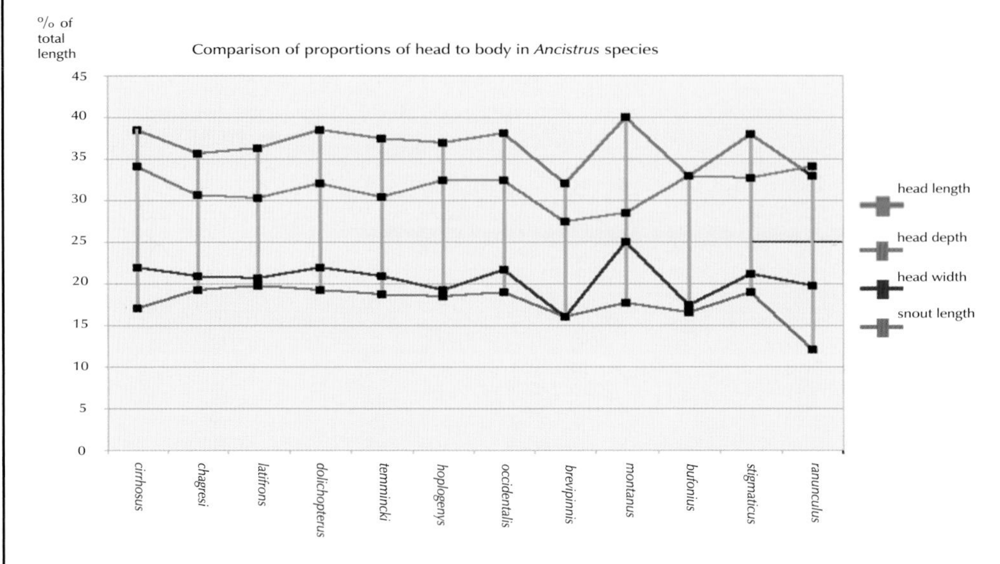

Figure 6.3: Comparison of head to body proportions between species.

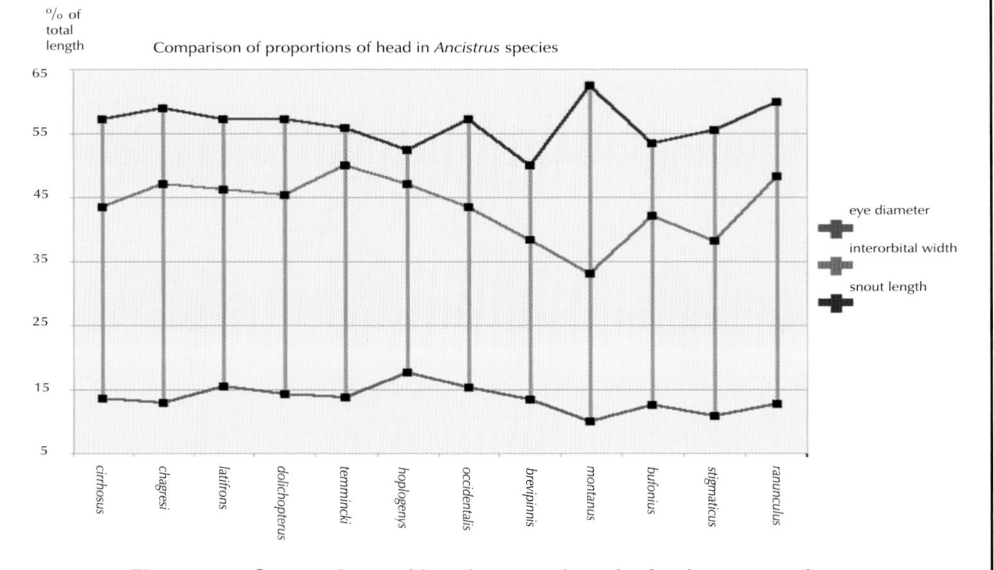

Figure 6.4: Comparison of head proportions in *Ancistrus* species.

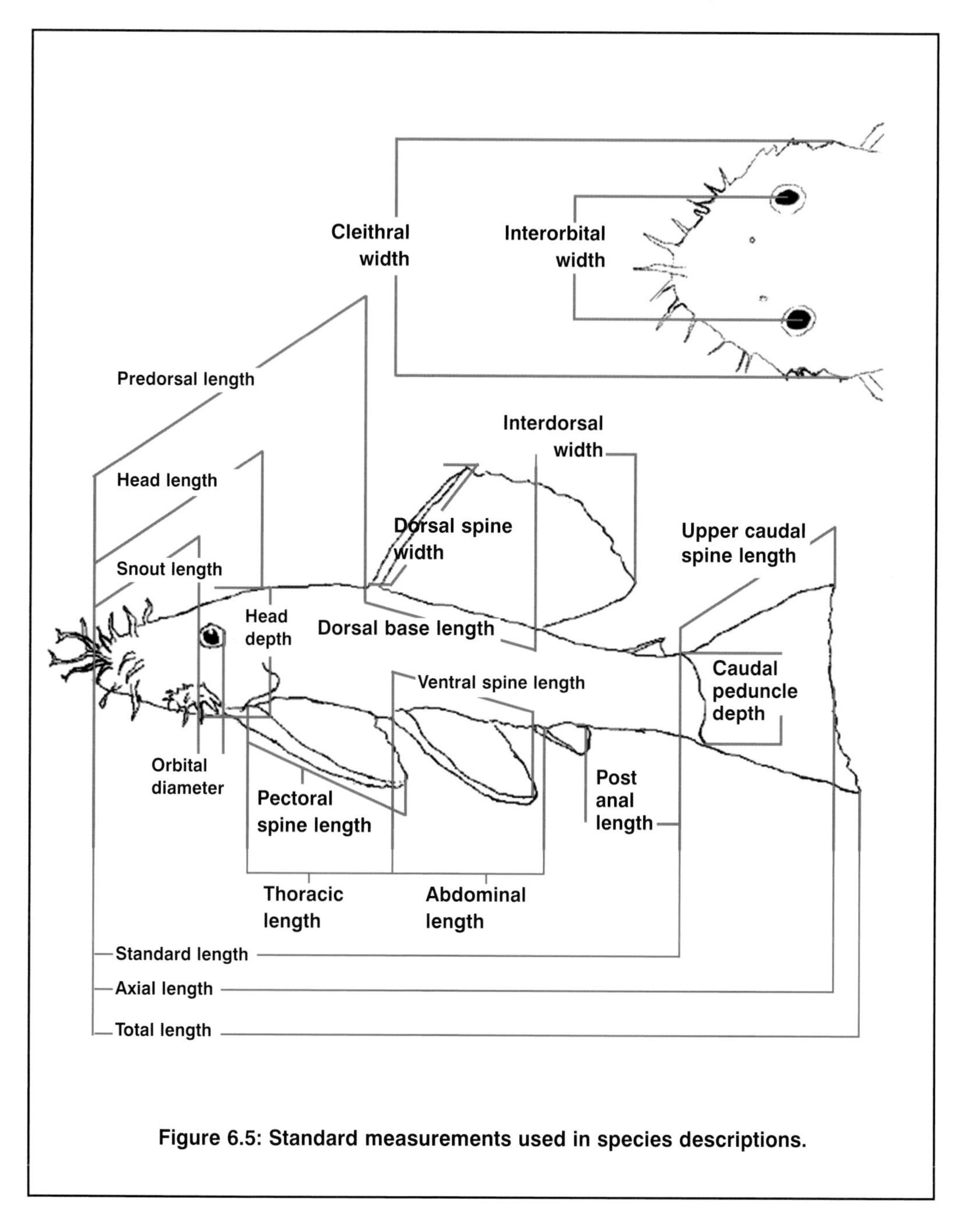

Figure 6.5: Standard measurements used in species descriptions.

in proportion to one another - instead of absolute values - the figures can be used to assess both large and smaller specimens. Figure 6.5 shows the typical measurements that are taken when describing a species.

We have photographs of those fish whose sole description has been as a number but most have little measurement information. Unfortunately, bristlenoses have characteristics of pattern that repeat regularly, such as pale spots on a dark background, and are prone to changing their background colour from dark to pale shades on a daily basis.

The bristles often vary between individuals of the same species, with some fish possessing forked bristles while others have only plain undivided ones. It is therefore not only difficult to sort out which species a particular individual should be assigned to but even to decide what constitutes a species when using only photographs.

Simplistically, a species could be defined as a group the members of which can breed together to produce viable offspring which are themselves capable of breeding, with the same characteristics as their parents. However, in many fish there are different varieties of the same species (for example the guppy or the goldfish) in which the members, although the same species, look totally different. They are nonetheless all still capable of breeding together successfully. Variations in colour and pattern can arise naturally which, if the variant fish breed together (as may happen in isolated populations) can become a distinct strain in which all the new generations have the same variation. (There are also many species of fish that naturally hybridise where their ranges meet; it is not known whether different *Ancistrus* species can interbreed.) This is the same process that drives evolution over massive time scales. Differences in appearance, especially where those differences are slight, do not necessarily mean a difference in species. Conversely, only slight differences do not necessarily indicate that the fish are the same species. There many examples of species of fish that share almost identical colour patterns but are nonetheless completely different species that do not breed together, even when they have the opportunity. There are probably many 'pairs' of bristlenoses that have frustrated their owners by never spawning which, in fact, would love to spawn if only they had a mate of the same species.

If you are selling fry or adults (and this applies to retailers too) it is far better to admit that you do not know what species it is than to make something up. Many different species often appear regularly in shops under the same name. The scientific names have become degraded into common names, albeit long ones, and can no longer be trusted to have any basis in fact.

Figure 6.6 Definitely NOT *Ancistrus multiradiatus*, a species name which is unknown in scientific circles.

The fish pictured in figure 6.6 was bought from an aquatic retailer under the name '*Ancistrus multiradiatus*'. This is not a valid name - there was once an *Ancistrus multiradiatus*, but it was reclassified and became *Liposarcus multiradiatus* (Hancock, 1828). This fish was obviously a true *Ancistrus*; a smaller male was already sprouting his bristles. Enquiries were made all the way back to the wholesalers who were adamant that the fish were *Ancistrus multiradiatus*. When it was pointed out to them that this fish did not exist they replied that it was a synonym (if they sold many, it is now) for *Ancistrus triradiatus*. In a spirit of helpfulness, they claimed it came from a tributary of the Rio Negro near Manaus. Not only is the fish nothing like a *triradiatus* but *triradiatus* have been found in Peru, Venezuela and Columbia. Emigres in Manaus are unlikely. The plot possibly thickens when one considers that Manaus is a commercial centre. Many fish are collected there for export; however, just because a fish left from Manaus does not necessarily mean it originated there. Doubtless the information given to me by both my retailer and his supplier was given in good faith but, like a game of Chinese Whispers, misinformation accrues around the fish throughout their journey. This does not mean that it is worthless asking for more information but the buyer needs to be prepared to discard some or all of it if it does not make sense. In the meantime the fish remains unidentified; like all bristlenoses, from time to time it looks like various L-numbers, merrily changing colour anywhere between pale fawn and deep brown as soon as I am close to settling on an identification.

Ancistrus temmincki and *Ancistrus cirrhosus* - the common bristlenose

The 'common' brown patterned bristlenoses which appear regularly in the shops are probably either *temmincki* or *cirrhosus*. *Cirrhosus* was named in a reference to the bristles, or cirrhi. Valenciennes originally described both species in 1840. The real credit for *temmincki* is generally ascribed to Gronovius, who described a *Plecostomus* (now an obsolete genus) in 1756 which may have been *A. temmincki*. A letter sent to Valenciennes by Monsieur Temminck describes the specimen:

It has *"the same spines, the same bristles and the same snout as those you have described; but the head is a little smaller, and rounder; the eyes are a little further apart and the pectoral spines reach almost to the middle of the ventrals."*

These proportions indicate a different species and are probably subject to the same variations as other *Ancistrus*. Valenciennes adds to this: *"The individual is four thumbs long, and in alcohol is a clear reddish-brown. The underside is white. I believe that this is the 'plecostomus' described by Gronovius."*

Figure 6.7: This female clearly exhibits the black spot at the base of the first dorsal fin ray. Unfortunately this is not a uniquely identifying characteristic for *cirrhosus*, being shared by other *Ancistrus* species.

In spite of these differences, *temmincki* and *cirrhosus* are very similar in appearance. The ground colour is a dark brown to which is added a pattern of paler irregular spots. Dark spots in the fins meet up to form cross bars. *Cirrhosus* has an obvious dark spot at the base of the first dorsal ray; temmincki is reputed to have less prominent light spots towards the tail. Unfortunately the dark spot in the dorsal is not rare among bristlenoses and the feature is also present in *A. chagresi* and others. *Cirrhosus* and *temmincki* have been given as synonyms in some aquarium books although Isbrucker upheld both species in his catalogue of the *loricariids*.

Originally, a good way of telling the two species apart was by their collection location. *Cirrhosus* was originally found in Buenos Aires while *temmincki* hailed from Surinam. Since that time many fish collectors have been active and both species are claimed to have been found in a number of countries. Although *temmincki* is not reported as far North as Uruguay, where *cirrhosus* can be found, nonetheless specimens of both are purported to have been found in Venezuela, Guyana, and Brazil.

Either both species are remarkably adaptable and have succeeded in establishing huge ranges of distribution or some of the documented museum specimens are misidentified. The volume of little tank-bred 'common bristlenoses' that appear in the shops with and without dorsal fin spots would indicate that both species are well suited to life as aquarium fish.

Ancistrus dolichopterus - the blue chin *Ancistrus*

Ancistrus dolichopterus was the first species to find general acceptance in aquarists' tanks and to be spawned in captivity. The resilient fish coped well in spite of being acclimated to low oxygen on a permanent basis. The fish was known as the 'blue chin' for being a very dark brown, almost black colour. It is described in early aquarium literature as having a white margin to the dorsal and caudal fins with a profusion of white spots over both the body and fins.

Strangely, in the original description of *Ancistrus dolichopterus*, Kner describes four fish; three were a uniform brown colour over the back and sides with regular light brown spots on the stomach. Only one male had spots on the back.

Although '*dolichopterus*' appears regularly in aquarium shops, these are probably usually either *temmincki* or *cirrhosus*. Although the 'common' bristlenoses do indeed have white edges to the dorsal and caudal fins when very young, these grow out rapidly. In adults the white has either disappeared completely or remains only as two flecks on the ends of the upper and lower caudal lobes. Fish retaining these markings in adulthood are rarely seen, as are fish with a colouring dark enough to have warranted the name of 'blue chin'. *A. dolichopterus* is notable for reaching a greater size, growing to about five inches instead of the more usual four inches for *temmincki* and *cirrhosus*.

In addition to the colour differences, *dolichopterus* can be differentiated by a longer dorsal fin which contains a larger number of fin rays than in most other species. Occasionally there are eight but, more often, nine. The species name means 'long fin'. The lower lobe of the tail is noticeably longer than the upper, being almost as long as the head. They also have fewer interopercular spines (between 6 and 9) than most other species.. By comparison, *cirrhosus* is excessively armoured, with between 9 and 13.

Ancistrus hoplogenys and others - a tale of confusion

When *Ancistrus hoplogenys* arrived in the aquarium trade it aroused great interest. Although the *cirrhosus, temmincki* and *dolichopterus* fish were, and still are, popular, the brown patterns are more subtle than striking. *A. Hoplogenys*, with its spatter of fine white spots on a jet black background, became known as the 'starlight plec' and sold for high prices before the current boom of interest in catfish. So striking was the fish that it was obviously inconceivable that the black with white spots pattern would occur in any other bristlenose species. However, as an ever growing variety of fish made their way into people's homes under the name of *hoplogenys*, it became obvious this was not the case. There are certainly several species with this basic colour pattern, with the spots ranging from a dusting so fine it could be mistaken for white spot infection to spots so large they look vaguely false.

Figure 6.8: Fish such as this one are often identified as *dolichopterus* but a photograph is not sufficient to make an identification with any reasonable hope of certainty.

Figure 6.9: Drawings of *Ancistrus dolichopterus* from Kner's type description (Denkschriften den Kaiserlichen Akademie de Wissenschaften 1854).

The fish described by Gunther in 1864 was a uniform blackish-brown, the belly being covered with fine white dots. The interopercular spines are shorter than those of *cirrhosus*, the longest being shorter than the diameter of the eye. There are usually eight or nine of these spines, compared to nine to thirteen for cirrhosus. The dorsal fin is higher than it is long; the length of the dorsal spine is less than the length of the head. The pectoral spine extends to the second third of the ventral fin.

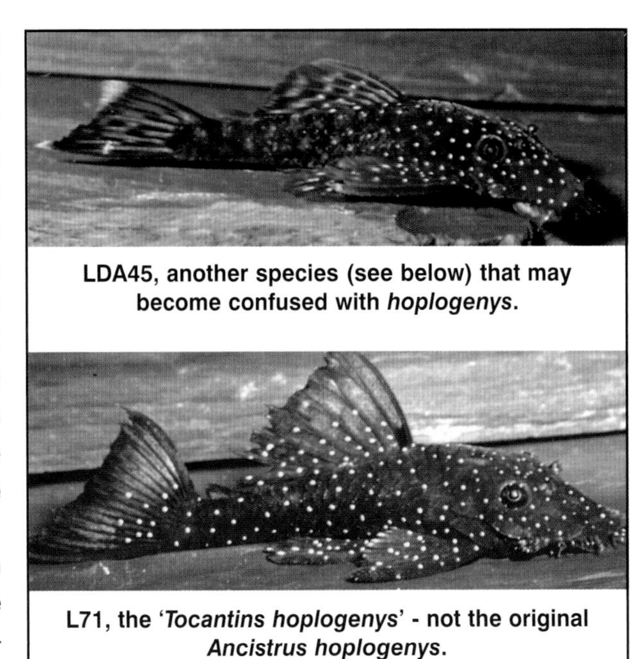

LDA45, another species (see below) that may become confused with *hoplogenys*.

L71, the '*Tocantins hoplogenys*' - not the original *Ancistrus hoplogenys*.

The fish that was most often seen in the aquarium trade would now be called a 'white-seam *Ancistrus*' and appears in the L number series as 183. Imports now seem to be far less reliable than they used to be; at one time healthy specimens would be found in aquarium shops, albeit at a high price. Over the last couple of years the species appears to have become progressively rarer and are more expensive and less healthy, often being hollow-bellied and fated for an early grave.

In volume five of the *Aquarium Atlas*, Baensch recognised the problem of multiple species under the same name; he referred to the fish as the '*hoplogenys* group'. Later in the text he points out that the 'group' is merely a convenience. Grouping fish together on the basis of what is a fairly common colour pattern, not only among *Ancistrus* but among other *Ancistrinae* genera, is as scientifically valid as a group called 'red fish' or 'stripy fish'.

The fish included in this 'group' by Baensch are listed as L4, L5 and L73. This is a strange choice because none of these are actually identified in the L-number series as *Ancistrus* although they are almost certainly members of the Ancistrinae. The list could be extended to cover a number of other Ancistrines. The *Ancistrus* species which fit the bill include L32, L43, L59, L71, L107, L125..... the list goes on for some while and demonstrates the point amply.

Being referred to as *hoplogenys* means that all the fish are regarded as having the same preferences. Given the wide number of species, it is to be expected that some of these will be more tolerant than others of harder waters and it is well worth trying a pair of black and white spotted fish even in a hard water area. Because of confusion among the species, spawning reports may or may not be relevant to the particular fish you have managed to buy. There is a great deal more to be discovered about the individual characteristics of all these species; any aquarists who have something to add to the information pool should make the effort to share it.

All the fish under the name of *hoplogenys* are tarred with the same brush and reputed to be rather shy and retiring, which I have found to be the case with the white-seam *Ancistrus*. This may be part of the reason for the unpleasant state of recent imports; they may find being packed into close quarters more stressful than their more ebullient cousins. However, another pair (possibly L120; most days a red seam on the dorsal and

Figure 6.13: This male exhibits none of the shy and retiring behaviour attributed to *A. hoplogenys*. Note the red edges to the caudal and dorsal and the red bristles. (Compare this photograph to Figures. 2.17 and 2.18 - it is the same fish.)

caudal is in evidence- the male also has red tips to his bristles!) which were sold to me as *hoplogenys* are anything but shy. They inhabit a community tank with two other pairs of different species and they are first to the front when food is around (or when they suspect it might be around, which is most of the time).

***Ancistrus ranunculus* - the black bushmouth**

The black bushmouth is an instantly recognisable fish. It vaguely resembles a bristlenose that hit a wall and was then run over by a steamroller. Coupled with having very blunt, broad heads, they are extremely flat and have a profusion of bristles growing forwards at an angle from the upper lip. Together with a rich velvety black colour, these features make them a conversation point in your aquarium. Their strange appearance has also earned them the common name of 'tadpole *Ancistrus*'; their scientific name is a reference to this, being derived from rana (a frog). This is one of the few fish that has made it out of the L-number series into proper scientific description - it is also known as L34 (and possibly L255).

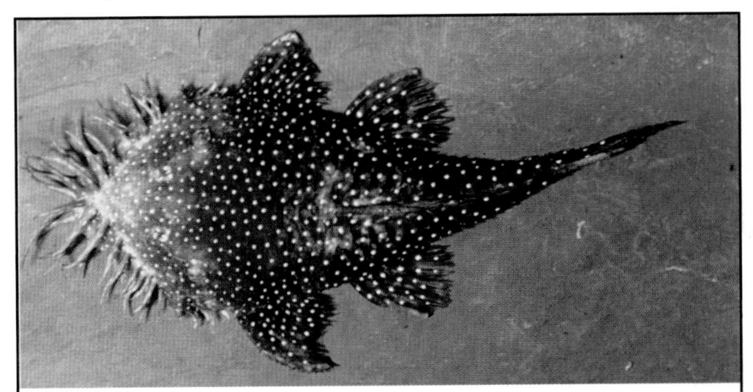

L255, possibly a variant of *Ancistrus ranunculus*.

Figure 6.14: The female (right) has a remarkable profusion of bristles, although not as many or as long as those of the male.

Physically they are unusual in several ways; apart from their distinctive shape they have the fewest teeth of any fish so far known in the genus. The females have remarkably prominent bristles; although they are not as profuse as those of the males, the difference is much more subtle than in most species. In both sexes the bristles are unbranched and thorn shaped.

Figure 6.15: The white blotch pattern is clear in the male.

Figure 6.16: This female *ranunculus* has a pattern of extremely fine white spots.

The general ground colour is a deep black. There may also be a pattern of six regular white blotches placed symmetrically with three on each side. The first and largest pair appears between the pectoral and ventral fins, with the last and smallest pair just before the tail. A white band appears at the caudal peduncle. Not all specimens show these blotches, and those that do do not show them all the time. This does not, however, appear to be a stress pattern. When the fish were removed from their aquarium for photographing, the pattern disappeared and only resumed as the fish became calmer. In the aquarium it is usually evident. Other specimens have a clear white flash on the end of the tail. L255, which may be a separate species or subspecies, also comes from the Xingu and is covered with clearly defined white spots. It does, however, strongly resemble the black *ranunculus* in body form and ground colour.

The fish pictured in Figures 6.15 and 6.16 also show an interesting colour variation although one which is remarkably difficult to photograph. Within a group of three males and two females, both the females proved to have a pattern of miniscule white spots, visible only in perfect lighting and from very close range. None of the males exhibited the spots. In a lone fish these tiny spots could easily be assumed to be a case of white spot; this is not the same pattern as shown in the obviously spotted L255. Since it is only visible with the fish in good light about six inches away, the colour form could pass unnoticed in other aquarium inhabitants. Examinations of a further group in an aquarium shop at the other end of the country also revealed that the solitary female was adorned with fine white spots. Without further specimens, it would be premature to draw further conclusions.

Figure 6.17: A young male gold marble *Ancistrus*.

Figure 6.18: A young female gold marble *Ancistrus*.

The fish is unusually sociable. In their home in the Rio Xingu they were found not only sharing the same crevices with other *ranunculus* but with a variety of other small peaceful *loricariids* and juveniles of larger species such as *Baryancistrus* species. Being so flat, they are able to make their homes in crevices that even other bristlenoses would find a tight fit. Their Xingu home provides them with shelter under flat stones on the bottom, in small passageways in rock piles, and even in cracks in submerged rocks. In the aquarium, slate is an ideal medium for housing them.

Although no bristlenoses naturally feed either on aquatic higher plants or land plants made accessible in the floods, the majority of species instantly recognise such items as cucumber and spinach as food. *A. ranunculus* usually regard these with complete disinterest, prefering live foods such as bloodworm. Fortunately their diet can be supplemented with higher bulk foods in the form of pellets and pre-soaked flake.

In bright light they are inactive, preferring to forage in dim light and at night. They share their natural habitat with *Hypancistrus zebra*, the zebra plec, and prefer the same conditions. Water temperatures should be around 80°F (although it should be remembered that temperatures in the Xingu can easily reach 90°F) and good filtration is essential. *Ancistrus ranunculus* have now been spawned in captivity; however this came as a surprise to the aquarist and no information is available about their brood care. This spawning occurred at a pH of between 6.6 - 6.8 and a temperature of 77°F.

LDA8 - the gold marble *Ancistrus*

The gold marble *Ancistrus* is a beautiful little fish, remarkable for its small size. The females tend to grow larger than the males, reaching a length of about 9cm. They are also very attractive with a pattern which is particularly strong in the males. A basic brown colour is topped with gold markings, comprising lines and dots on the head which fade out further down the body to be replaced by bands on the tail.

Originating from the Matto Grosso in Brazil, a pair could be kept in a smaller (100L) aquarium. They are tolerant in their water requirements and can be spawned in neutral to mildly alkaline water. The yellowish eggs are larger but less numerous than those of the bigger fish; a spawning comprises only up to 40 eggs.

Figure 6.19: Albino bristlenoses.

These little fish should not be kept in a group of larger *Ancistrus*, they would certainly lose out on the best nooks and crannies as well as the food. They are active and visible aquarium inhabitants; if not overawed by larger fish, they display typical bristlenose gluttony and are on the lookout for a meal at any time of day.

Figure 6.20: An unidentified female bristlenose.

Figure 6.21: *Ancistrus* sp.

Albino *Ancistrus* and colour mutations

A number of different fish that could be classified as true albinos (completely lacking in pigment) or leucistic (partially lacking in pigment) occur. One variation, known as the yellow or gold *Ancistrus*, is pinkish orange in colour with the ruby red eyes of the true albino. These fish can be spawned in aquaria and produce offspring of the same albino colouration. Very close examination of the fish reveals slightly darker orange spots and blotches. The mutation is rumoured to be naturally occurring. Another variation is reputed to have originated in the GDR from *Ancistrus dolichopterus*. This is a lighter yellow fish with more obvious

Figure 6.22: ***Ancistrus* sp.**

Figure 6.23: ***Ancistrus* sp.**

dark patterning; the first generation of a breeding results in all wild (dark) coloured fry, although subsequent inbreeding results in more albino fry. Another known variation is a yellow *Ancistrus* with white markings. The albino variations appear, from reports, to be somewhat more delicate than their normally coloured brethren. Some hobbyists have described low numbers of eggs and high mortality rates among the fry. Others are, however, breeding the fish successfully without problems.

A pale fish with normal dark eyes, which may be a variant of *Ancistrus temmincki*, was imported from Paraguay and given the number L144. In this fish the white flashes on the tail are still evident but the body is uniformly yellow-brown. A similar fish, listed as *Ancistrus tamboensis*, appears in '*Das Grose Buch Der Welse*' with a yellow-brown body and black eyes.

It seems apparent that colour mutations have occurred in a number of species, making appearance alone decidedly unreliable for identification of species.

Figure 6.24: *Ancistrus* sp.

Figure 6.25: *Ancistrus* sp.

The blind bristlenoses

Although unlikely to show up in your local aquarium shop due to the difficulty in collecting these subterranean species, the blind bristlenoses deserve a mention. Not only have the bristlenoses come up with the only known blind cave member of the *loricariids*, there are actually three separate species!

The first to be described was named *Ancistrus cryptophthalmus*, a reference to its hidden, dysfunctional eyes. This was described by Roberto Reis in 1987. Although the fish had been found prior to that, the specimens had been stored at the Museo 'Florentino Ameghino' in Argentina without further enquiry. Roberto Reis realised that these specimens represented an entirely new species and, in addition to the original twelve, was able to obtain five extra specimens. All the specimens were found in a cave in the Rio Sao Vicente system within the Tocantins drainage in Brazil.

Adaptation to a particular set of circumstances often produces similar results and the new *Ancistrus* species showed many adaptations common to cave-dwelling fish. Its pigmentation is reduced, although some faded colour remains. The eyes, although present in young fish, are slowly covered by skin as the fish grows. Cave-dwelling fish are often smaller than their above-ground counterparts and *A. cryptophalmus* appears to be no exception; the largest specimen was only was 78.6mm total length.

One blind bristlenose was already remarkable; in 1994 Alfredo Perez and Angel Viloria described *Ancistrus galani* from the Los Laurelos cave in the Venezuelan El Saman system. This species was named in honour of Carlos Galan, a Venezuelan biologist and speleologoist. The cave extends for a length of 1617 metres and it was only in the remote galleries that a single specimen of the new *Ancistrus galani* was found. Despite several later visits to the same area, only one other specimen could be discovered, so the species had to be described using only the two known specimens. Perez and Viloria carefully examined not only their new specimens but also the sighted *A. brevifilis* population living near the cave mouth, as it was important to determine that the blind fish were not just mutant *A. brevifilis*. The two proved to be different and Angel Viloria surmised that the cave population may have become isolated as long ago as the Pleistocene. Like *Ancistrus cryptophalmus*, the specimens were both small fish (the largest had a total length of 72.5mm), had very reduced pigmentation and absent or atrophied eyeballs. The overall colour of the fish is yellow; a last trace of pigment is noticeable in a dark spot behind the first ray of the dorsal fin. This is a characteristic of

Figure 6.26: *Ancistrus* sp.

Figure 6.27: *Ancistrus* sp.

Figure 6.28: *Ancistrus* sp. (dorso-lateral view). Photo: Dr D Sands

Figure 6.29a: Peruvian *Ancistrus* sp. (possibly *Ancistrus occloi*) from the Rio Vilcanota. Photo: Dr D Sands

Figure 6.29b: Peruvian *Ancistrus* sp. from the Rio Pachitea.
Photo: Dr D Sands

several ordinary *Ancistrus*, including the type species *A. cirrhosus*; it is interesting that this dark spot has been retained while other colour fades.

The El Saman system is nearly as far away from the Sao Vicente system as it is possible to get within the geographical range of *loricariids*. It is therefore almost certain that the two species evolved totally independently from different eyed *Ancistrus* ancestors. While fish on the surface have the option of swimming to new rivers, or being carried by predators, cave systems are isolated and fish cannot move from one to another. With now the only two troglodyte species from the *loricariids* to their credit, the bristlenoses added to their total with a third species, *Ancistrus formoso*, described in

1997 by Jose Sabino and Eleanora Trajano. Once again, finding enough specimens to describe the species proved problematic. The first was collected in 1995, in the Formoso cave system of the Matto Grosso. After a year, a second specimen was found in the Buraco do Ducho cave of the same system; these two specimens formed the basis of the description. Christened '*formosa*' after the cave system in which they were found, this species is the largest of the three troglodyte species, with one of the specimens reaching a total length of 108.1 mm. It is completely unpigmented - while *A. galani* and *A. cryptophalmus* exhibit some vestigial colour, *A. formosa* is completely pink.

While there are now plenty of recognised fish which are known to have adapted to an underground existence (such as the blind cave fish which is a common aquarium specimen), the *Ancistrus* have to contend with one major problem in their adaptation to a new life. *Ancistrus* are algae eaters - their mouths are designed for grazing across algal beds against the current and they have long guts to cope with the indigestible algae. Algae, although very simple examples, are plants. Plants feed by a process known as photosynthesis; if they are kept in the dark they cannot feed and will die. Therefore, the *Ancistrus* in their dark galleries are completely deprived of their major food source. In the pitch blackness, no plants can grow. This probably has a great deal to do with the small size of the troglodyte species but, in order to survive at any size, they need to have found some food from somewhere.

Both *Ancistrus formoso* and *Ancistrus cryptophalmus* are equipped with a comparatively large number of teeth. *A. cryptophalmus* is armed with up to 96 teeth in the upper jaw and up to 98 in the lower; *A. formoso* has up to 120 teeth in the upper jaw and up to 110 in the lower. This can be contrasted with eyed species from the Formoso basin with 59 upper and 56 lower. In a further modification, the teeth of *A. formoso* are not restricted to a single row; extras are randomly positioned behind the normal front row, and the teeth are abnormally long and slender. This modification may enable them to make use of food sources in the caves. Perhaps they use them as a sieve to extract particles from the cave substrate.

Appendix 1

Locations of *Ancistrus* specimens

The following table is a composite of various collections of *Ancistrus* specimens, designed to show the variety and extent of the known ranges as far as possible. No attempt has been made to verify the species identifications; these are the names under which they are lodged in assorted museums and described in various papers.

An asterisk indicates that the site listed refers to where the fish were imported from; the actual collection data is unknown and may or may not be in the vicinity of the offices of the exporter who collected them.

Ancistrus species	Country	Location notes
alga	Peru	Ambiyacu river
bodenhameri	Venezuela	Rio San Pedro
bolivianus	Bolivia	Rio Songo
baudensis	Colombia	Rio Baudo
brevifilis	Venezuela	Bolivar Zulia. Rio San Pedro at bridge S of Mene Grande, Motatan system. Aragua. Turmero Rio, near the town of Turmero. Miranda, Rio Guira. Anzoategui Bolivar Rio Coqollo, Sierra Perija El Concejo Apure

Ancistrus species	Country	Location notes
brevipinnis	Brazil	Rio Grande do Sul
bufonius	Peru Bolivia	Rio Apurimac La Merced or Puerto Bermudez Rio Colorado, 10m above Huachi
calamita	Peru Brazil	Rio Apurimac Amazonas, Rio Negro, Paricatuba (Nana Manaos)
caucanus	Colombia	Sonson, Cauca river basin
centrolepis	Panama Colombia	Darien, Rio Jesusito (source of R. Celorio) Truando Choco
chagresi	Panama Panama	Canal Zone, Rio Chagres Jesus Christ Stream, a trib. to Rio Chagres near Gamboa. Darien, Rio Tuira at Rio Mono, 130m
cirrhosus	Brazil Bolivia	Amazonas, Lago Jose Fernandes Amazonas, Rio Solimoes at Tabatinga (aka Sapurara). Goias, Barra do Rio Sao Domingos Para, Rio Amazonas delta at Gurupa. Para, Alcobaca Mato Grosso, Piraputanga Rondonia, Costa Marques, small trib. to Rio Guapore; Itenez - Mamore drainage. Beni, Huachi, at junction of Rio Bopi and Rio Cochabamba, elev. 2235ft

Ancistrus species	Country	Location notes
	Paraguay	Misiones Itapua, Arroyo Tembey, 7.4km by dirt road ca SW of San Rafael; Rio Parana drainage Paraguari, Arroyo Y by, at and below waterfall ESE of Ybycui. Canendiyu, Small arroyo at bridge 144km WSW of Salto del Guaira). Cordillera, Arroyo Piribebuy, 9.6km south (on paved rd) from Route 2 Concepcion, Arroyo Cagata at bridge. Amambay, Unnamed stream at bridge 3.4km south of route #5 at Chinguelo. Caazapa, Arroyo San Alfredo, 3.0km E on dirt road from Arroyo Ynaro bridge. Caaguazu, Arroyo Tobatiry, Rio Manduvira drainage. Canendiyu, Arroyo Itandey, trib. to Arroyo Carimbatay, 7.6km WSW of Curuguaty San Pedro, Rio Corrientes and adjacent flood pool.
	Guyana	Ireng Rio, near Holmia
	Venezuela	
	Uraguay	Canelones
clementinae	Ecuador	Los Rios, Rio de Clementina drainage: NW of Babahoyo
cryptophthalmus	Brazil	Sao Vicente drainage, Gruta do Passa Tres
damasceni	Brazil	Rio Grande do Sul, Santa Filomena

Ancistrus species	Country	Location notes
dolichopterus	Brazil Ecuador	Rio Negro, Paricatuba (Nana Manaos) Amazonas, Lago Badajos Para, Santarem
dubius	Brazil	Gurupa
erinaceus	Chile	
eustictus	Colombia	Rio Baudo
formoso	Brazil	Mato Grosso
fulvus	Brazil	Upper Rio Acara
galani	Venezuela	Los Laurales cave (Zu.31), Rio Socuy, Sierra de Perija
gymnorhynchos	Venezuela	Puerto Cabello Bolivar
heterorhynchus	Peru	Uruhuasi
hoplogenys	Guyana Peru Bolivia Ecuador Brazil	Rupununi, creek opposite Massara Island on Rupununi Rio. Gluck Island Loreto Puerto Suarez Beni Napo, Rio Conejo at Santa Cecilia. Napo, affluent from lower lake at Santa Cecilia. Para, Rio Capin

Ancistrus species	Country	Location notes
lineolatus	Colombia	Florencia Caqueta
lithurgicus	Guyana Brazil	Essequibo Rio at Crab Falls Rio Tapajoz, Pindobal Rio Acara in Thomme-Assu
macrophthalmus	Venezuela	Amazonas Orinoco Bolivar
maculatus	Brazil	Obidos
malacops	Ecuador Peru	Ambiyacu river
maracasae	Trinidad/Tobago	Maracas river
martini	Venezuela	San Antonio
mattogrossensis	Brazil	Mato Grosso
megalostomus	Bolivia	Huachi
melas	Colombia	Condoto
montanus	Brazil Bolivia	Rondonia, Costa Marques, small trib. to Rio Gaupore; Itenez - Mamore drainage. Tumupara Beni
multispinis	Brazil	Santa Catherina
nudiceps	Guyana	Takutu
occidentalis	Ecuador	Canelos

Ancistrus species	Country	Location notes
occloi	Peru	Cuzco, Rio Urubamba at Ollantaytambo (altitude 9,000ft)
pirareta	Paraguay	Paraguari Caaguaz, Rio Paraguay drainage Cordillera, Rio Paraguay drainage: Saltos de Piraret, above and below falls
piriformis	Paraguay	Rio Acaray, upper river Parana
planiceps	Panama	Darien
punctatus	Brazil	Rio Branco and Guapore, Mato Grosso
ranunculus	Brazil	Rio Xingu, Ilha de Kaituka Rio Xingu, Altamira Rio Xingu, Ilha de Babaquara Rio Tocantins, Maraba Rio Araguaia Rio Tocantins drainage
rothschildi	Venezuela	San Esteban
salgadae *scaphirhynchus*	Brazil Brazil	Ceara Amazonas, Rio Negro, Manaos area, white water river
spinosus	Panama	Panama, at culvert 11km E of Bayano Bridge on Carretera Panamericana. Darien, Rio Tuira at Rio Mono, 130m San Blas, Camp Sasardi, 12m Panama, Rio Frijoles drainage, Rio Frijolito

Ancistrus species	Country	Location notes
stigmaticus	Brazil	Goias Espirito Santo, Rio Sao Mateus at Sao Mateus. Sao Paulo
tamboensis	Peru	Rio Ucayali
taunayi	Brazil Uraguay	Rio Grande do Sul, Rio Forquilha Santa Catarina, Rio Jacutinga Itaqui Arroyo Arumbeba, approx 22km SE Artigas.
tectirostris	Peru	Ambiyacu river
temmincki	Guyana Brazil Peru Venezuela Surinam Paraguay	Rupununi, Moco-Moco Creek near Lethem. Packeoo Falls Para, Santarem Loreto, R. Nanay Bolivar
triradiatus	Venezuela Colombia Peru	Rio Tachira, 7km N of San Antonio, Catatumbo system. Portuguesa Barinas Meta, Rio Meta drainage: Rio Ocoa, ca 15km E of Villavicencio. Rio Magdalena Villavicencio
variolus	Peru	Rio Ambiyacu

Ancistrus species	Country	Location notes
L32	Brazil	Araguaia
L43	French Guiana	Mana
L45	French Guiana	Cacao
L59	Brazil	Ourem, Para
L71	Brazil	Santarem
L88	Brazil*	Manaus*/Belem
L89	Brazil*	Manaus*
L100	Brazil	Altamira
L107	Brazil*	Manaus*
L110	Brazil	
L111	Columbia	
L120	Guyana*	
L125	Venezuela*	
L144	Paraguay*	
L148	Venezuela*	Puerto Ayacucho*
L149	Venezuela*	Puerto Ayacucho*
L150	Venezuela*	Puerto Ayacucho*
L156	Brazil	Cameta, Rio Tocantins
L157	Brazil	Barcelos, Rio Negro
L159	Brazil	Rio Xingu
L180	Brazil	Rio Tocantins
L181	Brazil	Tefe
L182	Brazil	Rio Branco
L183	Brazil	Rio Negro
L184	Brazil	Rio Negro
L194	Venezuela	Calabozo
L213	Brazil	Pimental
L221	Brazil	Para
L223	Brazil	Para
L228	Brazil/Peru border	Javari

Literature

Trajano E and de Souza AM	1993	Behaviour of *Ancistrus cryptophalmus*, an armoured blind catfish from caves of Central Brazil, Mem. De Biospeologie, XXI, 151-159
Schaefer C	1996	Das Grosse Buch der Welse, bede-Verlag
Sabino J and Trajano E	1997	A new species of blind armoured catfish, genus *Ancistrus*, from caves of Bodoquena region, Mato Grosso do Sul, Southwestern Brazil, Rev. fr Aquariol. Herpetol, 24(3-4) 73-78
Reis RE	1987	*Ancistrus cryptophthalmus*, a blind mailed catfish from the Tocantins river basin, Brazil, Rev. fr Aquariol 14,3, 81-84
Perez A and Viloria A	1994	*Ancistrus galani*, n. sp. with comments on biospeleological explorations in western Venezuela, Mems. Biospeleol. v. 21:103-108
Riehl R and Baensch H	1991	Aquarium Atlas vol 5
Sabatino C	1998	Spawning of *Ancistrus ranunculus*, a hard to find newcomer, Tropical Fish Hobbyist May
Kobayagawa M	1991	The World of Catfishes, TFH
Stawikowski R	1998	Neu importiet: weitere Loricariiden aus dem Xingu, DATZ Jan

Sands D Dr	1984	Catfishes of the World vol 4
Graham JB	1983	The Transition to Air Breathing in Fishes II: effects of hypoxia acclimation on the bimodal gas exchange of *Ancistrus chagresi*, Journal of Exp. Biol., 102, 157-173
Graham JB and Baird T	1982	The Transition to Air Breathing in Fishes I: environmental effects on the facultative air breathing of *Ancistrus chagresi* and *Hypostomus plecostomus*, Journal of Exp. Biol. 96, 53-67
Gabriele VHL and Vollrath F	1998	Histological and Ultrastructural study of the stomach of the air breathing *Ancistrus multispinis*, Canadian Jnl Zool 6(1),83-86
Alexander R McN	1965	Structure and function in the catfish, J Zool 148, 88-152
Ono R Dana	1980	Fine structure and distribution of epidermal projections associated with taste buds on the oral papillae in some Loricariid catfishes, Jnl. Morph. 164:139-159
Blecknan H, Nienann U and Fritsch B	1991	Peripheral and central aspects of the acoustic and lateral line system of a bottom-dwelling catfish, *Ancistrus* sp. Jnl Comparative Neurology, 314(3) 451-466
Regan CT	1904	A monograph of the fishes of the family Loricariidae, Trans. Zool. Soc. London, 17(3):191-326
Francke H J	1980	Breeding the algae-eating bristlenose, TFH March

Boeseman M	1968	The genus *Hypostomus* and its Surinam representatives, Zool. Verh. Leiden, 99:1-89
Cuvier M Le B and Valenciennes MA	1840	Histoire Naturelle des poissons (15)
Sterba G	1973	Freshwater Fishes of the World, TFH
Muller S, Rapp Py-Daniel LH and Zuanon J	1994	*Ancistrus ranunculus*, a new species of loricariid fish from the Xingu and Tocantins rivers Ichthyol. Explor. Freshwaters v5 (4) 289-296 Dec
Kner R	1854	*Ancistrus dolichopterus* Denkschriften der Kaiserlichen Akademie de Wissenschaften
Gunther		*Chaetostomus hoplogenys*, Catalogue BM, v5
Buck S and Sazima I	1995	An assemblage of mailed catfishes (Loricariidae) in southeastern Brazil: distribution, activity, and feeding, Icthyol. Explor. Freshwaters, 6(4) 325-332
Power ME	1984	Depth distributions of armoured catfish: predator-induced resource avoidance? Ecology, 65(2) 523-528
Power ME	1984	The importance of sediment in the grazing ecology and size class interactions of an armoured catfish, *Ancistrus spinosus,* Env. Biol. Of Fishes 10(3) 173-181
Freihofer WC and Neil EH	1967	Commensalism between midge larvae (Diptera: Chironomidae) and catfishes of the families Astroblepidae and Loricariidae, Copeia, no 1, 39-45

Ferraris CJ, Isbrucker I and Nijssen H	1986	*Neblinicthys pilosus*, a new genus, and species of mailed catfish from the River Baria system, southern Venezuela, Rev fr Aquariol. 13, 3, 69-72
Howes J	1983	The cranial muscles of loricarioid catfishes, their homologies and value as taxonomic characters, Bulletin of the British Museum (NH) 45(6)
Montoya-Burgos JI, Muller S, Weber C and Pawlowski J	1997	Phylogenetic relationships between Hypostominae and Ancistrinae: first results from mitochondrial 12S and 16S rRNA gene sequences, Rev. Suisse de Zool. 104(1) 185-198
Isbrucker	1980	Classification and catalogue of the mailed Loricariidae, Versl. Techn. Gegevens, no 22, 181pp
Goulding M Leal, Carvalho M and Ferreira EG	1988	River Negro, Rich life in poor water, SPB Academic Publishing
Goulding M	1980	The Fishes and the Forest, University of California Press
Burgess WE	1989	An Atlas of Freshwater and Marine Catfishes, TFH
Mayland HJ	1994	Adventures with Discus, TFH
Sands D Dr	1994	The Behavioural and Evolutionary Ecology of *Corydoras adolfoi* and *Corydoras imitator*
Seidel I	1998	Transcript of discussion in aquanet chat room, aquanet, http://www.aquanet.de/

Index

A
Adaptations . . . 7, 21, 28, 30
Adult size . . . 55
Air pressure . . . 63-66
Albino . . . 48, 50, 90, 91-92
Ancistrinae . . . 10, 11, 12

B
Baensch . . . 85, 107
Binomial Nomenclature . . . 9
Blind bristlenoses . . . 92, 97, 98
Blotches . . . 88
Bogwood . . . 53, 54, 55, 58
Breathing . . . 27-28, 43, 51, 61
Bristles . . . 15, 32, 33, 34, 49, 80, 82

C
Catfish pellets . . . 7
Chaestoma . . . 12, 17, 18, 19, 26
Cirrhosus . . . 36, 82, 83, 84, 100
Colour . . . 49-50, 76, 80, 81, 82

D
Diet . . . 57-59, 62, 73-74, 98
Diseases . . . 59-61
Dolichopterus . . . 83-84, 91, 102

E
Eggs . . . 7, 62, 67, 68-73, 90
Eye . . . 22-23, 25, 46, 94

F
Filtration . . . 52, 53, 54, 71-73
Fin ray . . . 28-30
Floods . . . 42-43, 62
Fry . . . 70-75, 80
Fungus . . . 61, 70,

G
Gronovius . . . 82

H
Hatching . . . 71
Hiding . . . 6, 46, 49, 53, 55
Hoplogenys . . . 84-87, 102
Hypostominae . . . 12
Hypostomus . . . 17, 19, 26, 28

I
Ideal habitat (wild) . . . 38
Isbrucker, Dr . . . 11, 12, 76, 83, 110

L
LDA number series . . . 14

L-number. 13, 14, 76, 81, 85, 87
88-89, 92, 106
Lighting. 55, 59, 90
Linnaeus. 9
Loricariidae. 10, 11, 57

N

Neblinichthys 15

O

Overstocking 74

P

pH. 51, 57, 62, 90
Patches 50
Plants 55, 62, 89, 98
Power, Mary 43, 44
Proportions 77-78, 82

R

Ranunculus. 87, 88, 104

S

Sands, Dr D 63, 64, 108, 110
Scutes. 11, 16, 28, 30, 31, 50
Sexing. 32-34, 62, 87-88
Siluriformes 11
Spawning 43, 48, 56, 57
59, 62-75, 80
Spines 15-16, 21, 30-31,
45, 46, 56, 84
Squeaking 24
Standard measurements 79
Stomach. 17, 50
Substrate 53
Sucker mouth 25-26
Swim bladder 23, 24

T

Taming 59
Tank bred 48
Tank size 55
Taste buds 24-25, 26
Temperature 57
Territory 55-56

U

Undergravel filter 72

V

Valenciennes 82, 109

W

Weberian apparatus 24
White spot 60-61
Worms 60

X

Xenocara 12

Y

Yolk sac 73, 74